Impact maths 2 B

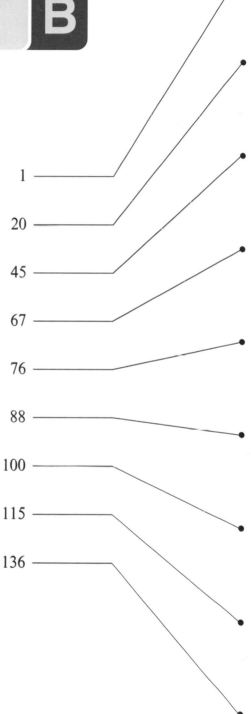

About this book

Impact maths provides a complete course to help you achieve your best in your Key Stage 3 Mathematics course. This book will help you understand and remember mathematical ideas, solve mathematical problems with and without the help of a calculator and develop your mental maths skills.

Exercises you should try without the help of a calculator are marked with this symbol:

Finding your way around

To help you find your way around when you are studying use the:

- **edge marks** shown on the front pages – these help you get to the right unit quickly

- **contents list** and **index** – these list all the key ideas covered in the book and help you turn straight to them.

- **links** in the margin – these show when an idea elsewhere in the book may be useful:

There is more about division on page 61.

Remembering key ideas

We have provided clear explanations of the key ideas you need throughout the book with **worked examples** showing you how to answer questions. **Key points** you need to remember look like this:

- **The distance around the edge of a shape is its perimeter.**

and are listed in a **summary** at the end of each unit.

Investigations and information technology

Two units focus on particular skills you need for your course:

- **using and applying mathematics** (unit 16) – shows you some ways of investigating mathematical problems.

- **calculators and computers** (unit 17) – shows you some ways of using calculators and computers and will help with mental maths practice.

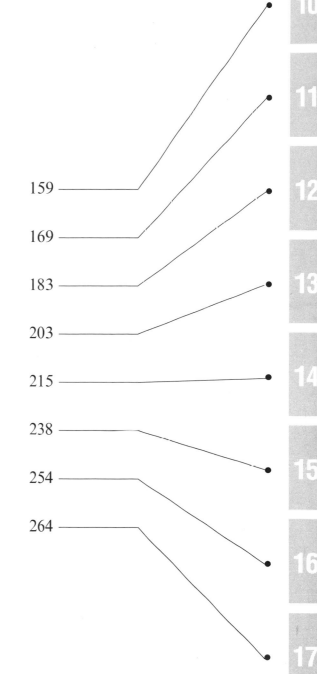

Heinemann Educational Publishers
Halley Court, Jordan Hill, Oxford, OX2 8EJ
a division of Reed Educational & Professional Publishing Ltd
Heinemann is a registered trademark of Reed Educational & Professional Publishing Ltd

OXFORD   MELBOURNE   AUCKLAND
JOHANNESBURG   BLANTYRE   GABORONE
IBADAN   PORTSMOUTH NH (USA)   CHICAGO

First published 1999

ISBN 0 435 01795 0

02 01
10 9 8 7 6 5

Designed and typeset by Tech-Set Ltd, Gateshead, Tyne and Wear
Illustrated by Barry Atkinson, Barking Dog and Tech-Set
Cover design by Miller, Craig and Cocking
Printed and bound by Edelvives, Spain

Acknowledgements

The publishers would like to thank Daniel Hunn for aviation information provided.
The authors and publishers would like to thank the following for permission to use photographs:

P11: Oxford Scientific films/Max Gibbs. P21: Science Photo Library/Mehau Kulyuk. P32: J. Allan Cash Ltd. P67: Science Photo Library/John Foster. P76: Science Photo Library/Alfred Pasieka. P90: Sonia Halliday Photographs. P100: Science Photo Library/Keith Kent; Science Photo Library/Professor Peter Goddard. P101: J. Allan Cash Ltd. P124: Empics Ltd/Tony Marshall. P136: Guggenheim Bilbao/Erika Barahona Ede. P160: Tony Stone Images; Tony Stone Images; Shaheen Hassan-Palin. P238: Robert Harding Picture Library.

Cover Photo by Tony Stone Images.

Publishing team

Editorial
Philip Ellaway
Nigel Green
Shaheen Hassan-Palin
Sarah Caton
Gwen Allingham

Design
Phil Richards
Colette Jacquelin
Mags Robertson

Production
David Lawrence
Joanne Morgan

Author team
David Benjamin
Tony Clough
Gareth Cole
Diana DeBrida
Ray Fraser
Peter Jolly
David Kent
Gina Marquess

Christine Medlow
Graham Newman
Sheila Nolan
Keith Pledger
Ian Roper
Mike Smith
John Sylvester

Tel:01865 888058   email:info.he@heinemann.co.uk

Contents

3   Multiplication and division

4   Working with algebra

5   Number patterns

6   Fractions

7 Probability

8 Decimals and percentages

9   Shape and measure

10   Positive and negative numbers

11   Graphs

1 Understanding number

1.1 Place value

You can write any number using the digits 0, 1, 2, 3, 4, 5, 6, 7, 8, 9. The value of each digit depends on its place in the number.

■ **To read large numbers it helps to put them in a place value diagram:**

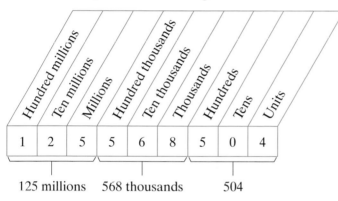

125 millions   568 thousands   504

The Population of Japan on one day in 1995 was 125 568 504 people

You say 'one hundred and twenty five million, five hundred and sixty eight thousand, five hundred and four'.

Example 1

What do the digits 4, 5, 6, and 7 mean in 762 154 839?

Think of the number in a place value table:

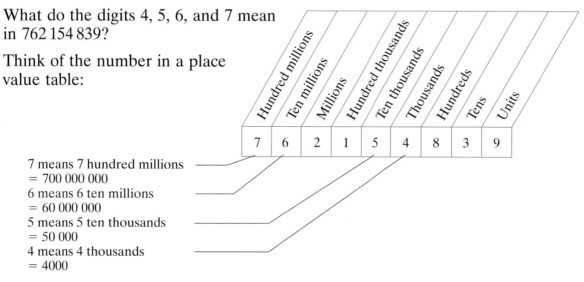

7 means 7 hundred millions
= 700 000 000
6 means 6 ten millions
= 60 000 000
5 means 5 ten thousands
= 50 000
4 means 4 thousands
= 4000

Example 2

How many millions are there in 762 154 839?

There are 762 millions in 762 154 839.

Hint: The gaps in the number show where the thousands and millions are:

762, 154, 839

Millions | Thousands

Exercise 1A

1 What does the 7 mean in each of these numbers?
  (a) 7 912 433   **(b)** 768 341 506   **(c)** 479 308 023
  (d) 78 500 643   **(e)** 45 873 922   **(f)** 58 783 900
  (g) 564 297 880   **(h)** 497 466 924   **(i)** 97 280 342

2 How many millions are there in each of these numbers?
  (a) 467 387 301   **(b)** 208 900 256   **(c)** 56 789 953
  (d) 6 560 089   **(e)** 45 600 897   **(f)** 45 078 899
  (g) 6 078 006   **(h)** 560 098 643   **(i)** 5 209 300

3 Write these numbers using digits:
  (a) Forty seven million, three hundred and sixty four thousand, seven hundred and fifteen.
  (b) Two hundred and twenty six million, seven hundred and ninety four thousand, one hundred and thirty.
  (c) Eight million, five hundred and sixteen thousand, two hundred and six.
  (d) Fifteen million, eight thousand, nine hundred and fifty six.

4 These pupils have been researching the World's seas.

Mine is eighty nine thousand, nine hundred square kilometres

Mine is two million, nine hundred and seventy thousand square kilometres

Mine is two million, five hundred thousand square kilometres

Tasneem   Bruce   Carl

Name of sea	Area in square kilometres
English Channel	89 900
Mediterranean	2 500 000
North	575 000
South China	2 970 000
Irish	88 500

  (a) Which sea has each pupil been researching?
  (b) The Bering sea has an area of two million, two hundred and sixty eight thousand, one hundred and eighty square kilometres. Write this number in figures.

Write this number in figures means write the number using digits.

1.2 Ordering numbers

Tasneem has been researching some of the world's largest islands. She wants to arrange them in order of size starting with the smallest.
She puts them into two groups:

group 1: areas in thousands of km^2

group 2: areas in millions of km^2

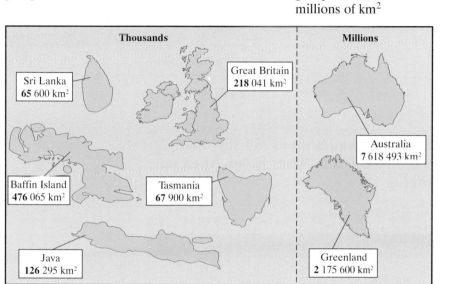

Each card shows the island's area in square kilometres: km^2.

There is more about areas on p. 216

She puts the 'thousands' group in order by looking at the number of thousands on each card; **65, 67, 126, 218, 476.**

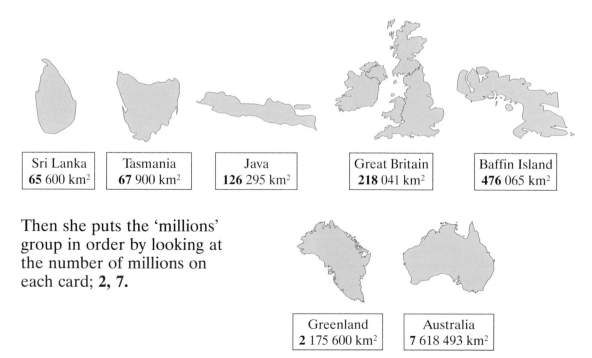

Sri Lanka	Tasmania	Java	Great Britain	Baffin Island
65 600 km^2	**67** 900 km^2	**126** 295 km^2	**218** 041 km^2	**476** 065 km^2

Then she puts the 'millions' group in order by looking at the number of millions on each card; **2, 7.**

Greenland	Australia
2 175 600 km^2	**7** 618 493 km^2

Now she can put her information into a table in order of size.

Island	Area in km^2
Australia	7 618 493
Greenland	2 175 600
Baffin Island	476 065
Great Britain	218 041
Java	126 295
Tasmania	67 900
Sri Lanka	65 600

■ **To order numbers larger than a thousand sort them into a thousands group and a millions group, then put each group in order.**

Exercise 1B

1 Make a table showing the populations of these cities in order of size:

Belfast 297 000

Edinburgh 411 000

Liverpool 852 000

Manchester 2 353 000

London 8 089 000

Bristol 552 000

Oxford 148 000

2 Rearrange these numbers in size order, smallest first:

89 900,   2 500 000,   88 500,   2 970 000,   575 000

3 Put the information showing the distance from the Sun of the first six planets into a table in order of size.

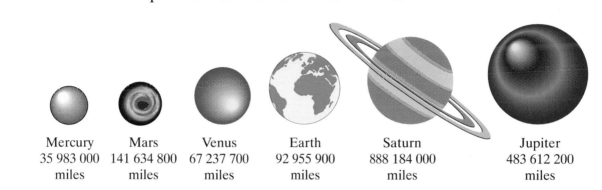

| Mercury | Mars | Venus | Earth | Saturn | Jupiter |
| 35 983 000 miles | 141 634 800 miles | 67 237 700 miles | 92 955 900 miles | 888 184 000 miles | 483 612 200 miles |

4 The table shows how many people followed different religions in Britain in 1989.
Rearrange in size order.

Religion	Followers
Presbyterians	1 346 000
Anglicans	1 928 000
Jews	108 000
Orthodox	231 070
Baptists	241 000
Roman Catholics	2 059 000
Hindus	150 000
Sikhs	200 000
Buddhists	25 000
Methodists	517 000
Muslims	900 000

1.3 Adding and subtracting multiples of 10, 100, 1000 . . .

■ **The multiples of 10 are the numbers in the 10 times multiplication table.**

$1 \times 10 = 10$
$2 \times 10 = 20$
$3 \times 10 = 30$
$\vdots \quad \vdots \quad \vdots$

Example 3

Work out $50 + 30$.

Think of $5 + 3 = 8$

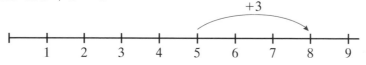

Now make all the numbers 10 times larger:

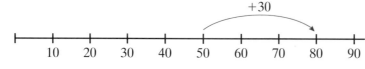

So $50 + 30 = 80$.

To find $500 + 300$ just make the numbers 100 times larger:

So $500 + 300 = 800$.

Similarly $5000 + 3000 = 8000$.

You need to take care when adding or subtracting a mixture of multiples for example, to do $500 + 30$

Think of $50 + 3 = 53$

Now make all the numbers 10 times larger.

So $500 + 30 = 530$

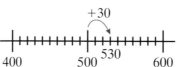

Example 4

Calculate:

(a) $700 - 500$ (b) $15\,000 - 8000$ (c) $7000 - 600$

(a) $7 - 5 = 2$
so $700 - 500 = 200$

(b) $15 - 8 = 7$
so $15\,000 - 8000 = 7000$

(c) $70 - 6 = 64$
so $7000 - 600 = 6400$

Exercise 1C

Calculate:

1 (a) $40 + 50$
   (c) $200 + 700$
   (e) $80 + 60 + 90$
   (g) $5000 + 7000$

   (b) $70 + 80$
   (d) $6000 + 3000$
   (f) $900 + 600$
   (h) $500 + 900 + 400$

2 (a) $80 - 50$
   (c) $70 + 90 - 50$
   (e) $8000 - 6000 + 2000$
   (g) $400 - 600 + 500$

   (b) $9000 - 2000$
   (d) $500 + 200 - 300$
   (f) $50 - 70 + 60$
   (h) $80 - 300 + 400$

   Hint: think of this as $50 + 60 - 70$

3 (a) $400 + 60$
   (c) $7000 - 900$
   (e) $800 - 60$
   (g) $400 + 500 - 30$

   (b) $400 - 70$
   (d) $6000 + 700$
   (f) $5000 + 300$
   (h) $6000 + 900 - 200$

4 Here is a route from **Start** to **Finish** through the grid of numbers. The finishing number is:
$200 + 30 + 100 + 2000 + 80 = 2410$

   (a) Find the route which gives the largest finishing number.
   (b) Find the route which gives the smallest finishing number.

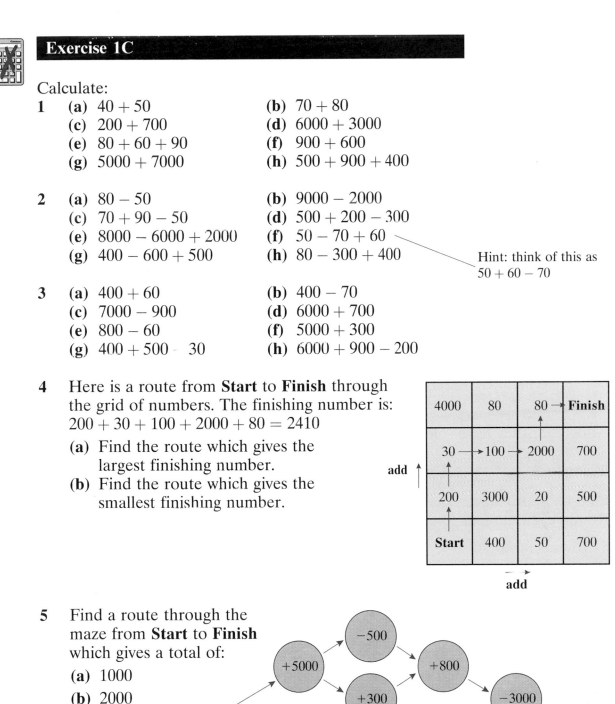

5 Find a route through the maze from **Start** to **Finish** which gives a total of:

   (a) 1000
   (b) 2000
   (c) 3000
   (d) 4000
   (e) Find the route which gives the closest total to 5000.

1.4 Rounding numbers to the nearest 10

Tasneem, Bruce and Carl are selling tickets for their swimming club.

To find an approximate total they round their numbers to the nearest 10.

■ **To round to the nearest 10:**
Look at the digit in the units column.
If it is less than 5 round down.
If it is 5 or more round up.

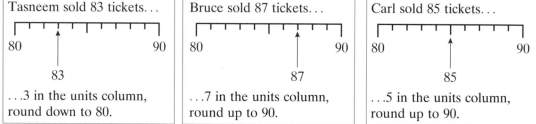

Tasneem sold 83 tickets...

80   90

83

...3 in the units column, round down to 80.

Bruce sold 87 tickets...

80   90

87

...7 in the units column, round up to 90.

Carl sold 85 tickets...

80   90

85

...5 in the units column, round up to 90.

Altogether they have sold about $80 + 90 + 90 = 260$ tickets.

Example 5

Find an approximate answer for $87 + 52$.
Round each number to the nearest 10 then add.

87 rounds up to 90
52 rounds down to 50
So $87 + 52$ is about $90 + 50 = 140$.

Example 6

Arthur sold 70 tickets for the school lottery, rounded to the nearest 10. How many tickets might Arthur have actually sold?

The smallest number that rounds to 70 is 65

The largest number that rounds to 70 is 74

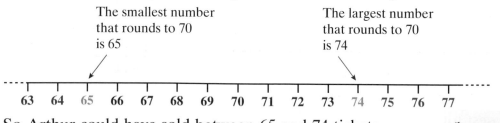

63   64   65   66   67   68   69   70   71   72   73   74   75   76   77

So Arthur could have sold between 65 and 74 inclusive.

'between 65 and 74 inclusive' means you include 64 and 75.

Exercise 1D

1 Round each of these numbers to the nearest 10:
   (a) 49   **(b)** 72   **(c)** 34   **(d)** 85   **(e)** 83   **(f)** 57
   (g) 56   **(h)** 51   **(i)** 35   **(j)** 99   **(k)** 16   **(l)** 96

2 Approximate each of these numbers to the nearest 10:
   (a) 248 **(b)** 363 **(c)** 584   **(d)** 275   **(e)** 752   **(f)** 633
   (g) 697 **(h)** 501 **(i)** 894   **(j)** 596   **(k)** 437   **(l)** 295

Hint:
Round to . . .
Approximate to . . .
Write correct to . . .
all mean the same
thing.

3 Write each of these numbers correct to the nearest 10:
   (a) 1439   **(b)** 6572   **(c)** 4397   **(d)** 3795
   (e) 8491   **(f)** 7996   **(g)** 3998   **(h)** 14 264
   (i) 17 345   **(j)** 18 698   **(k)** 24 997   **(l)** 29 998

4 Round each number to the nearest 10 then add or
   subtract to get an approximate answer.
   (a) 43 + 88   **(b)** 29 + 45
   (c) 87 − 38   **(d)** 72 − 29
   (e) 82 + 56 + 39   **(f)** 89 + 62 − 29
   (g) 14 + 68 + 33   **(h)** 198 − 56 − 72

5 Tasneem, Bruce and Carl have been
   selling tickets again. They each
   rounded the number of tickets they
   sold to the nearest ten.
   How many tickets could each have
   actually sold?

6 This table shows how many calories are in
   100 grams of different types of meat, rounded to
   the nearest ten.
   (a) How many calories could each actually have?
   (b) Bacon has 271 calories per 100 grams.
        How would this be written in the table?
   (c) Ham has 168 calories per 100 grams.
        How would this be written in the table?

Meat	Calories
Beef	220
Chicken	140
Lamb	350
Pork	330

7 The tallest dam in Europe is the Grande Dixence in
   Switzerland. It is 290 metres tall to the nearest 10 metres.
   What is the smallest height it could actually be?

8   The world's tallest structure was the Warszawa Radio
Mast which collapsed in 1991. It was 650 metres tall to
the nearest 10 metres.
What is the tallest height it might actually have been?

1.5 Rounding to the nearest 100 or 1000

Megan, Selima and Dean have been
raising money for charity.

To find an approximate total they all
rounded their amounts to the
nearest £100.

■   **To round to the nearest 100:**
Look at the digit in the tens column.
If it is less than 5 round down.
If it is 5 or more round up.

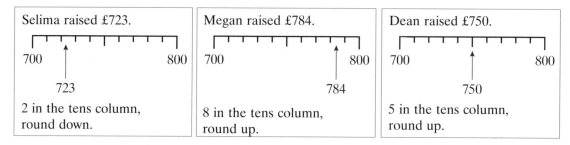

Selima raised £723.

700   800

723

2 in the tens column,
round down.

Megan raised £784.

700   800

784

8 in the tens column,
round up.

Dean raised £750.

700   800

750

5 in the tens column,
round up.

Altogether they raised about £700 + £800 + £800 = £2300

Similarly:

■   **To round to the nearest 1000:**
Look at the digit in the hundreds column.
If it is less than 5 round down.
If it is 5 or more round up.

Example 7

Find an approximate answer to $783 + 519 + 250$.
Round each number to the nearest 100 then add.

    783 rounds up to   800
    519 rounds down to   500
    250 rounds up to   300 +
                           ‾‾‾‾
                           1600

So $783 + 519 + 250$ is about 1600.

Example 8

Find an approximate answer to $6945 + 8501 - 4098$.
Round each number to the nearest 1000 then add.
Split the calculation into two stages:

6945 rounds up to 7000   Answer to first stage 16 000
8501 rounds up to 9000 +   4098 rounds down to 4000 −
$\overline{16\,000}$ $\overline{12\,000}$

So $6945 + 8501 - 4098$ is about 12 000.

Example 9

There are 2500 different species of catfish in the world, rounded to the nearest 100. How many different species might there actually be?

The smallest number that rounds to 2500 is 2450.

The largest number that rounds to 2500 is 2549.

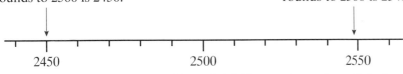

2450   2500   2550

So there are between 2450 and 2549 species of catfish in the world.

Exercise 1E

1 Round each of these numbers to the nearest 100.
(a) 583   (b) 261   (c) 728   (d) 351
(e) 78   (f) 609   (g) 1238   (h) 2482
(i) 14 513   (j) 993   (k) 4209   (l) 9963

2 Round each number to the nearest 100, then add or subtract to find an approximate answer to the calculation.
(a) $682 + 246$ (b) $458 + 298$ (c) $838 - 491$
(d) $670 - 153$ (e) $847 + 682$ (f) $962 - 413$
(g) $719 - 482$ (h) $609 - 185$ (i) $893 - 642$
(j) $1817 - 384$ (k) $2154 - 805$ (l) $1984 - 462$

3 Write each of these numbers to the nearest 1000.
(a) 2843   (b) 7624   (c) 6287   (d) 9051
(e) 4523   (f) 12 731   (g) 28 604   (h) 111 640
(i) 9833   (j) 842   (k) 257   (l) 99 524

4 Round each number to the nearest 1000, then add or subtract to find an approximate answer to these calculations.

(a) $8287 - 3724$

(b) $9831 - 4296$

(c) $5523 + 3058$

(d) $8399 + 1502$

(e) $9398 + 2485$

(f) $6721 - 924$

(g) $4086 + 2589$

(h) $9487 + 3521$

(i) $14\,287 - 3944$

(j) $18\,437 + 8521$

(k) $26\,714 - 12\,387$

(l) $29\,841 + 7203$

5 George, Katie and Omar have been collecting signatures on a petition. They each rounded their numbers to the nearest 100. How many signatures might each have collected?

6 The table shows the number of people killed in earthquakes in 1994.
Write each number rounded to the nearest 100.

Country	Killed
Algeria	171
Colombia	269
Indonesia	215
USA	57

7 The table shows the number of people killed in earthquakes in Turkey this century to the nearest 1000.

(a) What is the smallest number of people that might have been killed in each year?

(b) What is the greatest number of people that might have been killed in each year?

Year	Killed
1992	2000
1939	23 000

8 The table shows the height of the five tallest volcanoes in the world.

(a) Write the height of each volcano rounded to the nearest 100 metres.

(b) Write the height of each volcano rounded to the nearest 1000 metres.

Name	Location	Height
Aconcagua	Argentina	6960
Kilimanjaro	Tanzania	5930
Popocatépetl	Mexico	5483
Ararat	Turkey	5198
Klyuchevskoy	Russia	4850

1.6 Checking answers by estimating

Sasha used her calculator to add $783 + 519 + 1250$. Has she got the right answer?

783 rounds up to	800
519 rounds down to	500
1250 rounds up to	1300 +
	2600

The answer is about 2600 so Sasha has got the wrong answer.

■ **You can check to see if a calculator answer is correct by rounding to get an approximate answer.**

Rounding to get an approximate answer is called **estimating**.

Example 10

Which number in the cloud is the correct answer to $573 + 246$?

7119 621
819 327

573 rounds to	600
246 rounds to	200 +
	800

so 819 must be the correct answer.

Exercise 1F

1 Which number in the cloud is the correct answer?

(a) $487 + 246$

1093 733
241
913

(b) $813 - 469$

652 1282
164
344

(c) $829 + 752$ 1581   1401   1041   77

(d) $883 - 524$ 359   259   1407   759

(e) $791 - 254$ 537   637   1045   1315

(f) $267 + 384$ 351   117   651   451

2   Use rounding to help you see which calculator shows the correct answer:

(a) $8841 - 2314$

(b) $9488 + 4815$

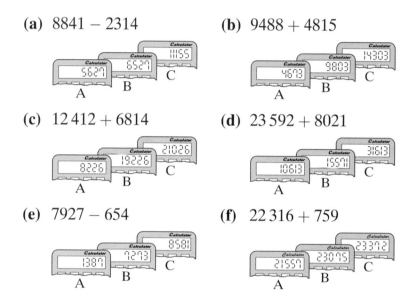

(c) $12\,412 + 6814$

(d) $23\,592 + 8021$

(e) $7927 - 654$

(f) $22\,316 + 759$

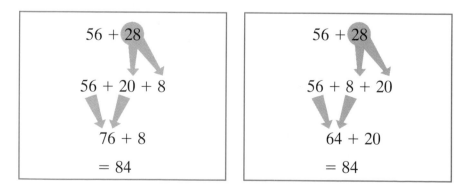

1.7 Mental maths with 2-digit numbers

This section reminds you how to add and subtract 2-digit numbers mentally.

Here are two different ways to do $56 + 28$:

$56 + 28$	$56 + 28$
$56 + 20 + 8$	$56 + 8 + 20$
$76 + 8$	$64 + 20$
$= 84$	$= 84$

Here are three ways to do 74 − 26:

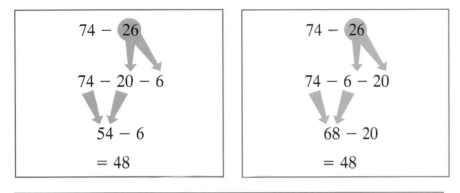

74 − 26

74 − 20 − 6

54 − 6

= 48

74 − 26

74 − 6 − 20

68 − 20

= 48

Start at 26 and work out how much you must add to get to 74.

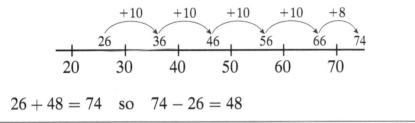

$26 + 48 = 74$ so $74 − 26 = 48$

Exercise 1G

Calculate:

1 (a) $45 + 24$ (b) $56 + 32$ (c) $73 + 16$ (d) $34 + 25$
   (e) $43 + 53$ (f) $27 + 48$ (g) $35 + 57$ (h) $46 + 28$
   (i) $39 + 23$ (j) $27 + 47$ (k) $38 + 48$ (l) $43 + 29$

2 (a) $82 + 34$ (b) $93 + 25$ (c) $77 + 42$ (d) $65 + 83$
   (e) $84 + 54$ (f) $86 + 48$ (g) $79 + 63$ (h) $94 + 57$
   (i) $65 + 85$ (j) $87 + 43$ (k) $68 + 94$ (l) $73 + 87$

3 (a) $47 − 14$ (b) $68 − 23$ (c) $96 − 34$ (d) $74 − 32$
   (e) $85 − 43$ (f) $43 − 25$ (g) $62 − 36$ (h) $74 − 49$
   (i) $86 − 38$ (j) $93 − 52$ (k) $78 − 29$ (l) $46 − 27$

4 (a) $29 + 48 + 14$ (b) $34 + 65 − 46$
   (c) $47 + 28 − 32$ (d) $34 + 28 + 27$
   (e) $47 + 38 − 59$ (f) $46 + 37 + 46$
   (g) $38 + 35 + 88$ (h) $66 − 27 + 86$
   (i) $83 − 65 + 77$ (j) $76 − 29 − 28$

5 Max has £100 to spend on computer software.

    (a) He could buy Space Pilot, Maths Pack and F-1 Racing. How much would these three cost in total?

    (b) What other combinations can he afford to buy and how much does each cost in total?

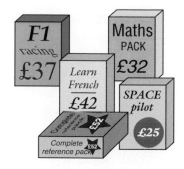

6 The table shows the scores of four pupils in three tests.

    (a) What was the total score of each pupil?

    (b) What was the difference between the best score and the worst score in each test?

Name	French 1	French 2	French 3
Philbert	46	35	42
Louise	31	22	38
Ashton	47	42	39
Magnus	26	19	28

1.8 Adding numbers on paper

This section reminds you how to add numbers on paper.
To do $683 + 594 + 87$:

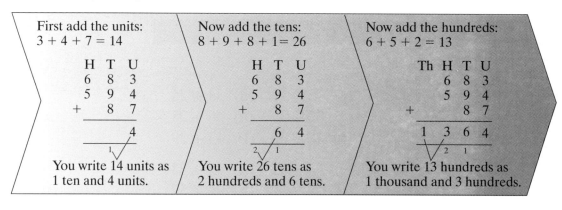

First add the units:
$3 + 4 + 7 = 14$

```
  H  T  U
  6  8  3
  5  9  4
+    8  7
─────────
        4
       1
```

You write 14 units as
1 ten and 4 units.

Now add the tens:
$8 + 9 + 8 + 1 = 26$

```
  H  T  U
  6  8  3
  5  9  4
+    8  7
─────────
     6  4
   2  1
```

You write 26 tens as
2 hundreds and 6 tens.

Now add the hundreds:
$6 + 5 + 2 = 13$

```
  Th H  T  U
     6  8  3
     5  9  4
  +     8  7
  ──────────
   1  3  6  4
     2  1
```

You write 13 hundreds as
1 thousand and 3 hundreds.

Exercise 1H

You should do these questions using pencil and paper.

1 Calculate:

    (a) $563 + 354$ **(b)** $439 + 236$

    (c) $564 + 378$ **(d)** $587 + 165$

    (e) $436 + 162 + 35$ **(f)** $568 + 154 + 56$

    (g) $368 + 44 + 57$ **(h)** $786 + 547 + 694$

    (i) $657 + 278 + 849$ **(j)** $847 + 978 + 846$

2 The table shows the number of people using a swimming pool during a week in April.

(a) How many people went swimming each day?

(b) What was the total number of people who went swimming in the afternoon at the weekend?

(c) What was the total number of people who went swimming on the evenings of Wednesday, Thursday and Friday?

Week beginning 7th April			
Day	Morning	Afternoon	Evening
Monday	78	109	217
Tuesday	83	165	198
Wednesday	125	98	252
Thursday	97	152	215
Friday	102	147	253
Saturday	257	298	147
Sunday	142	368	Closed

1.9 Subtracting numbers on paper

To do $635 - 382$:

First subtract the units: $5 - 2 = 3$	You can't subtract 8 from 3...	... so change 1 hundred into 10 tens: $13 - 8 = 5$	Now subtract the hundreds: $5 - 3 = 2$
H T U 6 3 5 − 3 8 2 ——— ⎵ ⎵ 3	H T U 6 3 5 − 3 8 2 ——— ? 3	H T U ⁵6̸ ¹3 5 − 3 8 2 ——— 5 3	H T U ⁵6̸ ¹3 5 − 3 8 2 ——— 2 5 3

You can use the same method to subtract a 2-digit number from a 3-digit number.

$$\begin{array}{r} \text{H T U} \\ {}^{8}\cancel{9}\,{}^{13}\cancel{4}\,{}^{1}6 \\ -\quad\ \ 6\ \ 9 \\ \hline 8\ \ 7\ \ 7 \end{array}$$

Always remember to line up the units.

Exercise 1I

You should do these questions using pencil and paper. Calculate:

1 (a) $675 - 342$ (b) $534 - 217$

(c) $657 - 284$ (d) $833 - 241$

(e) $792 - 384$ (f) $837 - 258$

(g) $753 - 484$ (h) $576 - 38$

(i) $266 - 78$ (j) $704 - 245$ ——— Hint: Change the 7 hundreds into 6 hundreds and 10 tens

2 The table shows part of the records of an antique dealer. It shows the price at which she bought and sold each antique.

Antique	Bought for	Sold for
Clock	£87	£215
Mirror	£58	£136
Chest	£435	£821
Table	£394	£760
Chair	£168	£225

(a) How much **profit** did she make on each item?

(b) At an auction she bought a pair of bookcases for a total of £437. She later sold one of them for £350 and the other for £364. What was her total profit on the bookcases?

(c) At the same auction she bought a desk for £363 and a swivel chair for £85. She later sold them together for £734. What was her profit?

Profit is:
selling price – buying price

Summary of key points

1 To read large numbers it helps to put them in a place value diagram.

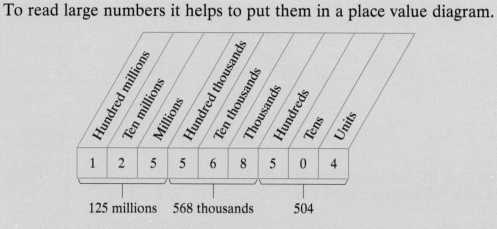

125 millions   568 thousands   504

2 To order numbers larger than a thousand sort them into a thousands group and a millions group, then put each group in order.

3 The multiples of 10 are 10, 20, 30, 40, . . .
They are the answers in the 10 times multiplication table.

4 To round to the nearest 10:
Look at the digit in the units column.
If it is less than 5 round down.
If it is 5 or more round up.

To the nearest 10:
442 is 440

less than 5,
round down

5 To round to the nearest 100:
Look at the digit in the tens column.
If it is less than 5 round down.
If it is 5 or more round up.

> To the nearest 100:
> 4263 is 4300
> ╱
> 5 or more
> round up

6 To round to the nearest 1000:
Look at the digit in the hundreds column.
If it is less than 5 round down.
If it is 5 or more round up.

7 You can check to see if a calculator answer is correct by rounding to get an approximate answer.

2 Symmetry and angles

2.1 Rotations and reflections

Many shapes in nature have symmetry:

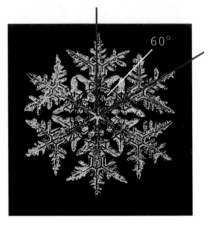

If you hold a mirror on this line, the snowflake will look the same. It has **reflective symmetry**.

The snowflake looks the same after a rotation of 60°.
It has **rotational symmetry**.

■ **A shape has rotational symmetry if it looks exactly the same after a rotation.**

Remember: a rotation is a turn.

This shape has rotational symmetry:

This point is the **centre of rotation.**

It looks the same as the original shape 3 times in a complete turn.

The **order** of rotational symmetry is 3.

■ **The order of rotational symmetry is the number of times a shape looks exactly the same in a full turn.**

Example 1

Find the order of rotational symmetry of this shape:

Step 1: trace the shape. Mark one vertex.

Step 2: put a point in the centre of rotation on the tracing paper and turn the paper until you get a shape that looks the same.

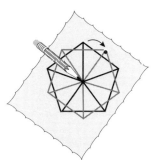

Step 3: repeat step 2 until the marked vertex is back where it started.

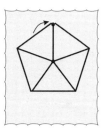

Count how many times the shape looks the same.

The traced shape fits on top of the original 5 times before it is back where it started.
The order of rotational symmetry is 5.

Exercise 2A

Find the order of rotational symmetry for each shape:

1   **(a)**   **(b)**   **(c)**   **(d)**

(e)   **(f)**   **(g)**   **(h)**

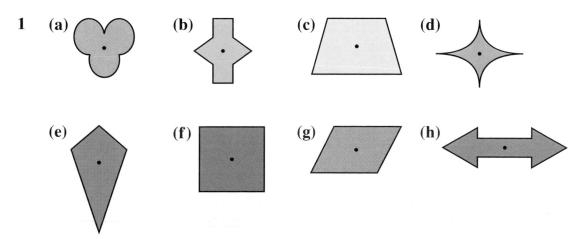

2 For each shape find:
- The number of lines of symmetry
- The order of rotational symmetry

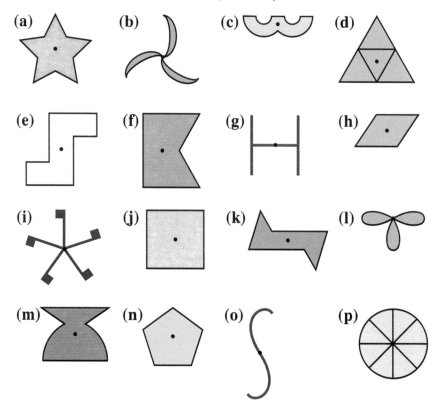

3 Say which of the shapes in question **1** have reflection symmetry.

2.2 Angles

■ **An angle is a measure of turn.**
Angles are usually measured in degrees, ° for short.

The angle between two lines is the amount of turn needed to move one line onto the other.

This angle is 133°:

You would have to turn the red line through 133° for it to be on top of the blue line.

Hint:
You say 'one hundred and thirty three degrees'.
You write 133°.

133°

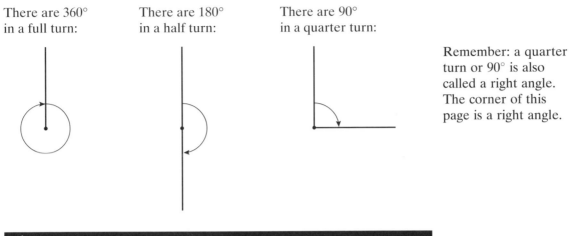

There are 360°
in a full turn:

There are 180°
in a half turn:

There are 90°
in a quarter turn:

Remember: a quarter
turn or 90° is also
called a right angle.
The corner of this
page is a right angle.

Exercise 2B

Approximately how many degrees are there in each of these turns?
Choose your answers from this list:

20°   45°   100°   190°   270°   300°

1   **2**   **3**   **4**   **5**   **6**

2.3 Angle types

■ **Angles less than 90° are called acute angles.**

■ **Angles greater than 90° but less than 180° are called obtuse angles.**

■ **Angles greater than 180° are called reflex angles.**

Example 2

Name these angles:

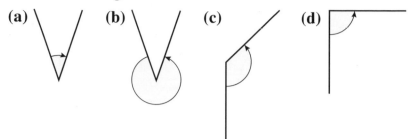

(a) Is an acute angle because it is less than 90°.
(b) Is a reflex angle because it is greater than 180°.
(c) Is an obtuse angle because it is between 90° and 180°.
(d) Is a right angle because it is exactly 90°.

Exercise 2C

Without measuring, write down the angle types of these angles.

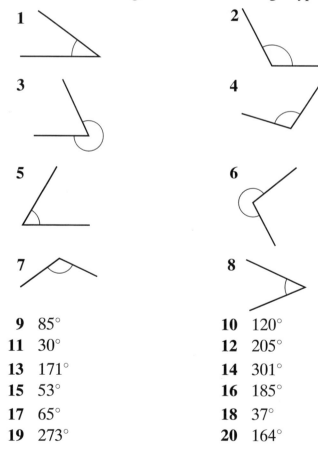

9 85°	**10** 120°
11 30°	**12** 205°
13 171°	**14** 301°
15 53°	**16** 185°
17 65°	**18** 37°
19 273°	**20** 164°

2.4 Measuring angles

You can use a protractor to measure angles:

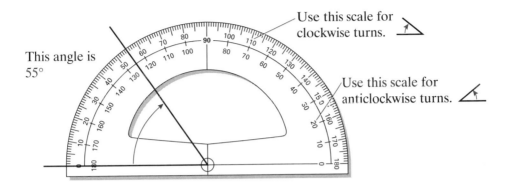

This angle is 55°

Use this scale for clockwise turns.

Use this scale for anticlockwise turns.

Exercise 2D

1 Use a protractor to measure these angles:

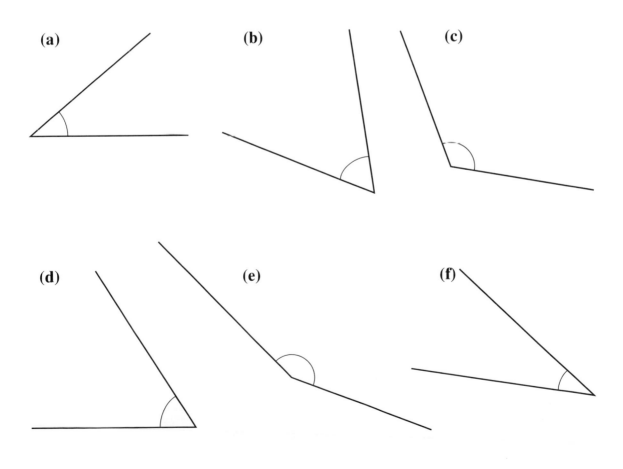

(a)

(b)

(c)

(d)

(e)

(f)

(g) **(h)** **(i)**

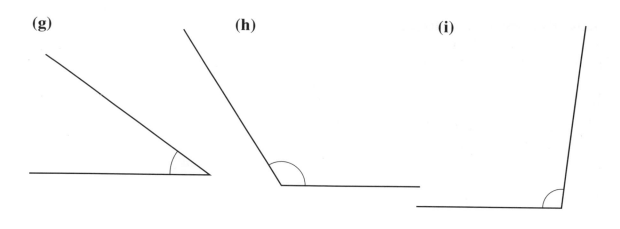

(j) **(k)** **(l)**

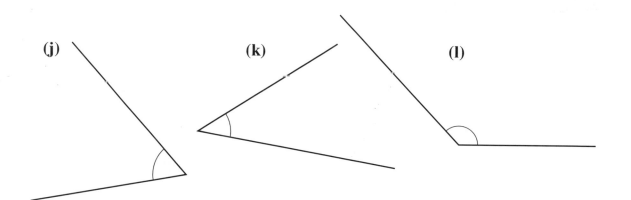

Measuring reflex angles

Example 3

Measure the red angle:

You can't measure it directly with a protractor so measure the smaller (blue) angle:

It is $58°$.

There are $360°$ in a full turn. So the larger (red) angle is $360° - 58° = 302°$.

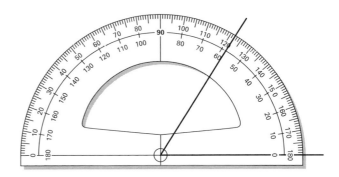

■ **To measure a reflex angle, measure the smaller angle and subtract it from 360°.**

Exercise 2E

1 Measure these angles with a protractor.

(a)

(b)

(c)

(d)

(e)

(f)

(g)

(h)

(i)

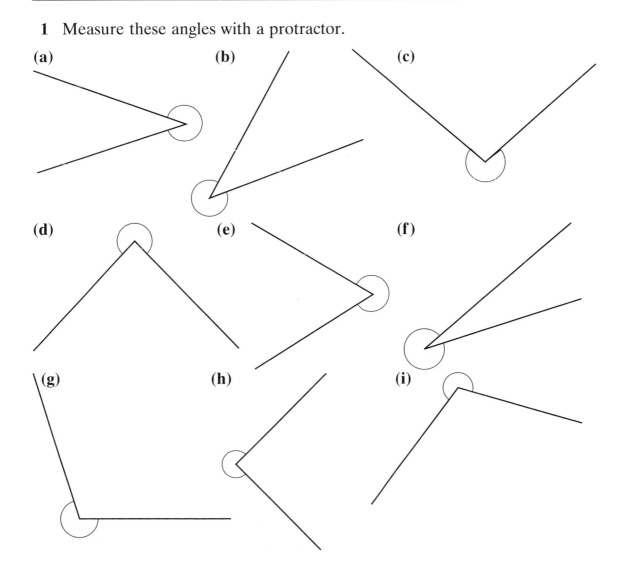

2.5 Drawing angles

You can use a protractor to draw angles too.

Example 4

Draw an angle of 145°.

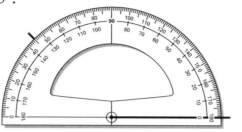

Draw a straight line

Put your protractor on the line so that the cross is at the end. Make a mark at 145°

Join the mark to the line to make the angle.

Example 5

Draw an angle of 300°.

300° is a reflex angle. A normal protractor only measures up to 180°. To draw 300° you draw the angle that makes up a full turn:

$$360° - 300° = 60°$$

300° is the outside angle:

Remember: there are 360° in a full turn.

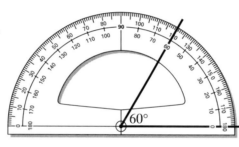

$$300° + 60° = 360°$$

Exercise 2F

Use a protractor to help you draw these angles:

1 30°	**2** 75°	**3** 50°	**4** 100°	**5** 75°
6 200°	**7** 25°	**8** 265°	**9** 120°	**10** 82°
11 145°	**12** 167°	**13** 115°	**14** 250°	**15** 65°
16 335°	**17** 28°	**18** 133°	**19** 98°	**20** 312°

2.6 Estimating angles

You can already say if an angle is acute, obtuse or reflex.
You need to be able to estimate the size of an angle more
precisely.

Example 6

Estimate the size of these angles:

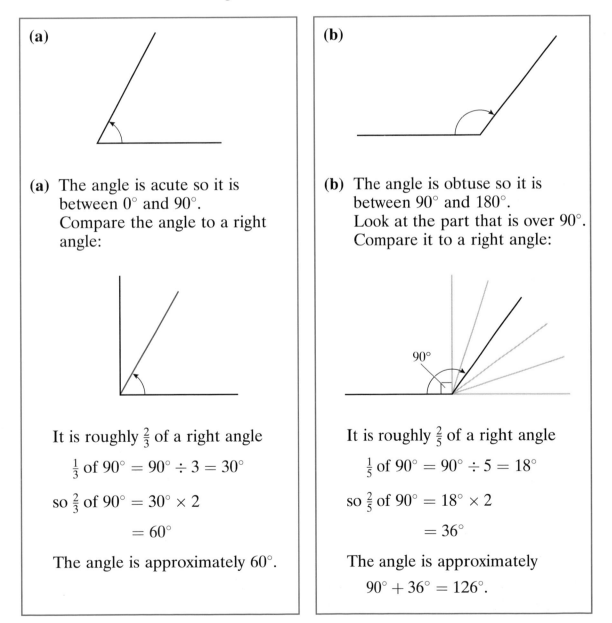

(a) The angle is acute so it is
between $0°$ and $90°$.
Compare the angle to a right
angle:

It is roughly $\frac{2}{3}$ of a right angle

$\frac{1}{3}$ of $90° = 90° \div 3 = 30°$

so $\frac{2}{3}$ of $90° = 30° \times 2$

$= 60°$

The angle is approximately $60°$.

(b) The angle is obtuse so it is
between $90°$ and $180°$.
Look at the part that is over $90°$.
Compare it to a right angle:

It is roughly $\frac{2}{5}$ of a right angle

$\frac{1}{5}$ of $90° = 90° \div 5 = 18°$

so $\frac{2}{5}$ of $90° = 18° \times 2$

$= 36°$

The angle is approximately

$90° + 36° = 126°$.

Exercise 2G

1 For each angle:
- write the type of angle: acute, obtuse or reflex
- estimate the size of the angle.

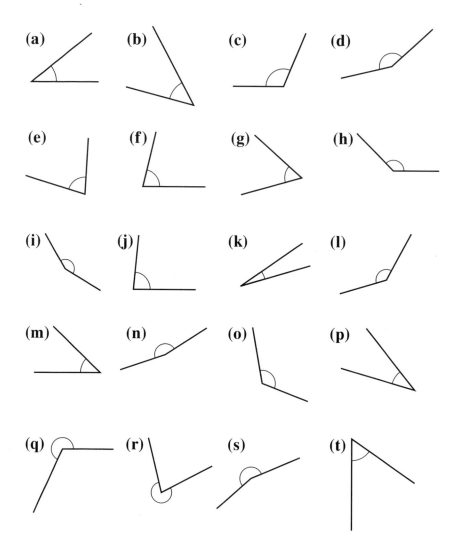

2.7 Angles on lines

You can put two or more angles
together to make a corner:

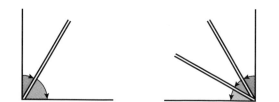

■ **Angles in a corner add to 90°**

You can also put two or more angles together to make a straight line:

■   **Angles on a straight line add to 180°**

You can use these facts to find missing angles in diagrams.

Example 7

Find the missing angles:

(a)

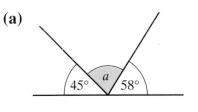

(b)

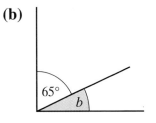

(a) $45° + a + 58° = 180°$
so $a + 103° = 180°$
so $a = 180° - 103°$
$a = 77°$

(b) $65° + b = 90°$
so $b = 90° - 65°$

$b = 25°$

Exercise 2H

Find the missing angles:

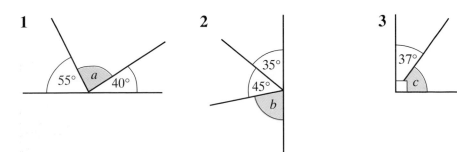

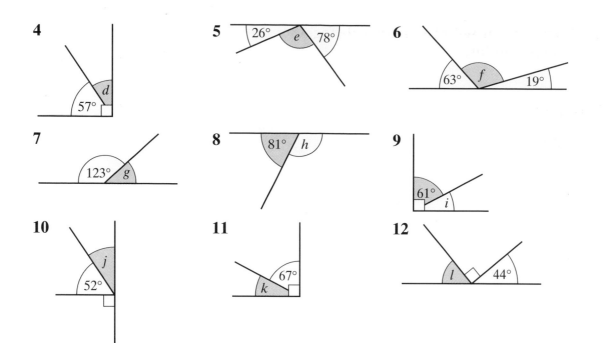

4

d

$57°$

5

$26°$ e $78°$

6

$63°$ f $19°$

7

$123°$ g

8

$81°$ h

9

$61°$ i

10

j

$52°$

11

$67°$

k

12

l $44°$

2.8 Angles at a point

There are 360° in a full turn.
You can fit angles together to make a full turn.
The angles must add up to 360°

■ **Angles at a point add to 360°.**

Example 8

Find the missing angle:

$126°$ a
$88°$

$126° + 88° + a + \ 90° = 360°$
so $\qquad a + 304° = 360°$
so $\qquad a \qquad = 360° - 304°$

$a = 56°$

There are 20 sections on a dart-board. The angles add to 360°.

Remember:

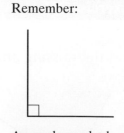

An angle marked
like this is a right
angle.

■ **When two straight lines cross the opposite angles are equal.**

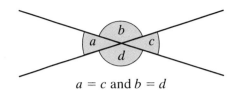

$a = c$ and $b = d$

Example 9

Find the missing angles:

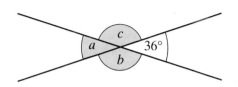

Give reasons for your answers.

$a = 36°$ (opposite angles are equal)

$b + 36° = 180°$ (angles on a straight line add to $180°$)

$b \quad = 180° - 36°$

$b \quad = 144°$

$c \quad = 144°$ (opposite angles are equal)

Exercise 2I

Find the missing angles.
Give reasons for your answers.

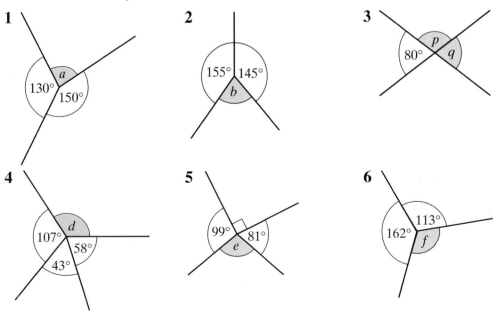

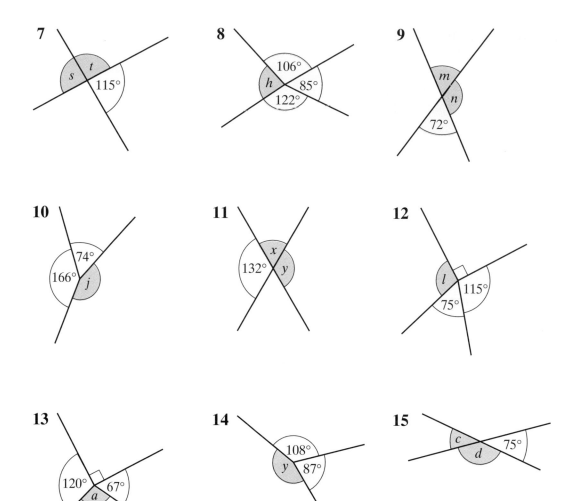

7 s t 115°

8   106° h 85°   122°

9 m n 72°

10   74°   166° j

11 x 132° y

12 l 115°   75°

13   120° a 67°

14   108° y 87°

15 c d 75°

2.9 Angles in shapes

You will see angles in shapes written in two different ways:

Type 1
Using a letter

Type 2
Using the points that make the angle

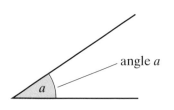

angle a

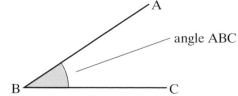

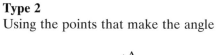

A

angle ABC

B   C

Example 10

From the diagram:
(a) use points to describe angle *a*
(b) use a letter to describe angle XYZ.

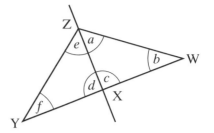

(a) Angle *a* is at Z.
  Using points it is WZX
          or XZW.

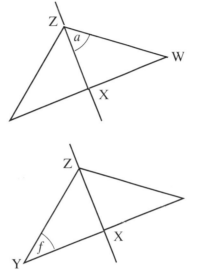

(b) Angle XYZ is angle *f*.

Exercise 2J

1 Use points to describe the marked angle in each diagram.

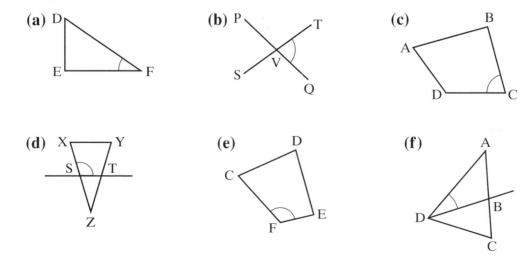

2 Write down the single letter which describes the angle named below each shape.

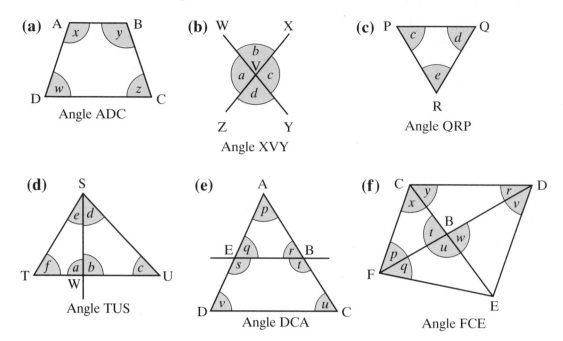

(a) Angle ADC

(b) Angle XVY

(c) Angle QRP

(d) Angle TUS

(e) Angle DCA

(f) Angle FCE

2.10 Triangles and quadrilaterals

A triangle is a shape with three sides and three angles.

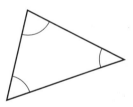

A quadrilateral is a shape with four sides and four angles.

Activity

Draw any triangle on a piece of paper.
Use a ruler.

Colour the three angles, then cut them out:

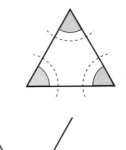

Fit the angles together:

What do you notice?

Repeat the activity for a quadrilateral:

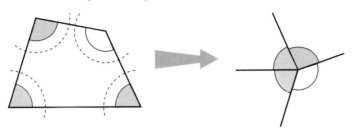

- **The angles of a triangle add to 180°**
- **The angles of a quadrilateral add to 360°**

You can use these facts to find missing angles in shapes.

Example 11

Find the missing angles:

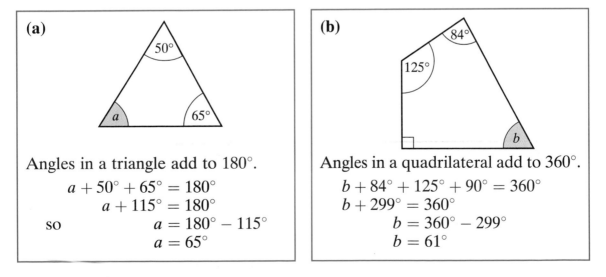

(a)

Angles in a triangle add to 180°.

$$a + 50° + 65° = 180°$$
$$a + 115° = 180°$$
so $$a = 180° - 115°$$
$$a = 65°$$

(b)

Angles in a quadrilateral add to 360°.

$$b + 84° + 125° + 90° = 360°$$
$$b + 299° = 360°$$
$$b = 360° - 299°$$
$$b = 61°$$

Exercise 2K

1 Find the missing angles:

(a)

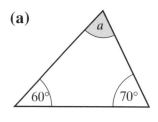

(b)

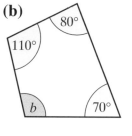

(c)

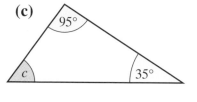

(d)

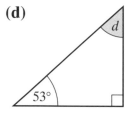

(e)

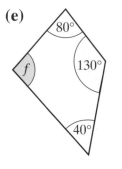

(f)

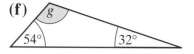

(g)

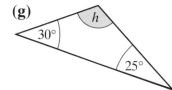

(h)

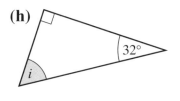

(i)

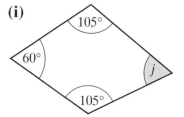

(j)

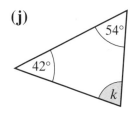

(k)

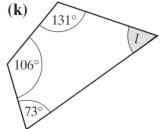

(l)

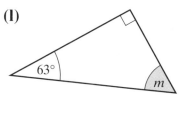

(m)

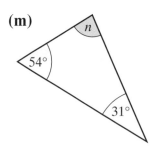

(n)

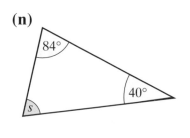

(o)

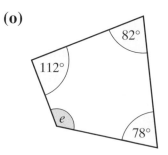

2.11 Angles in polygons

A **polygon** is another name for a shape with straight sides. Some polygons have special names:

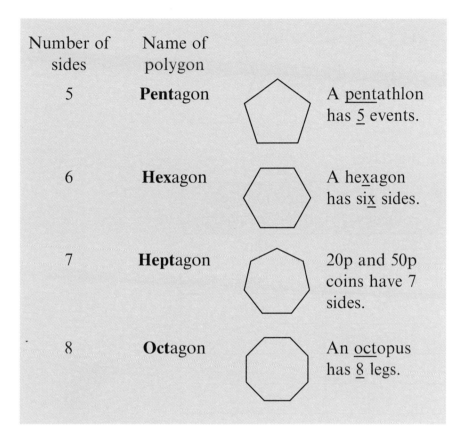

Number of sides	Name of polygon		
5	**Pent**agon		A <u>pent</u>athlon has <u>5</u> events.
6	**Hex**agon		A he<u>x</u>agon has si<u>x</u> sides.
7	**Hept**agon		20p and 50p coins have 7 sides.
8	**Oct**agon		An <u>oct</u>opus has <u>8</u> legs.

Poly is the Latin word for many. Polygon means 'many sided'.

You can find the sum of angles in a polygon by splitting it into triangles.

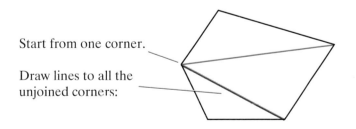

Start from one corner.

Draw lines to all the unjoined corners:

The pentagon is made up of 3 triangles.

The sum of the angles in a triangle is $180°$

So the sum of the angles in a pentagon is

$$180° \times 3 = 540°$$

Exercise 2L

1 For each shape:
- Name the shape.
- Work out the sum of the angles inside the shape.

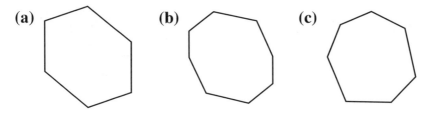

(a)   **(b)**   **(c)**

2 Copy and complete this table:

Shape	Number of sides	Sum of angles inside the shape
Triangle	3	180°
Quadrilateral	4	360°
Pentagon	5	540°
Hexagon	6	
Heptagon	7	
Octagon	8	

3 Find the missing angles:

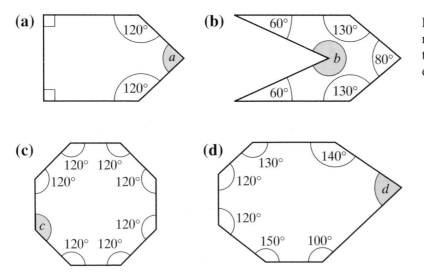

(a) 120°, 120°, *a*

(b) 60°, 130°, 60°, 130°, *b*, 80°

Hint: first count the number of sides. Use the angle total from question 2.

(c) 120° 120°, 120°, 120°, 120°, *c*, 120° 120°

(d) 130°, 140°, 120°, *d*, 120°, 150°, 100°

2.12 Regular polygons

■   **A regular polygon has equal sides *and* equal angles.**

These polygons are regular:

These polygons are not regular:

All sides and angles are equal.

Not all sides and angles are equal.

■   **The angles inside a shape are called interior angles.**
    The angles outside a shape are called exterior angles.

■   **In any polygon:**
    interior angle + exterior angle = 180°

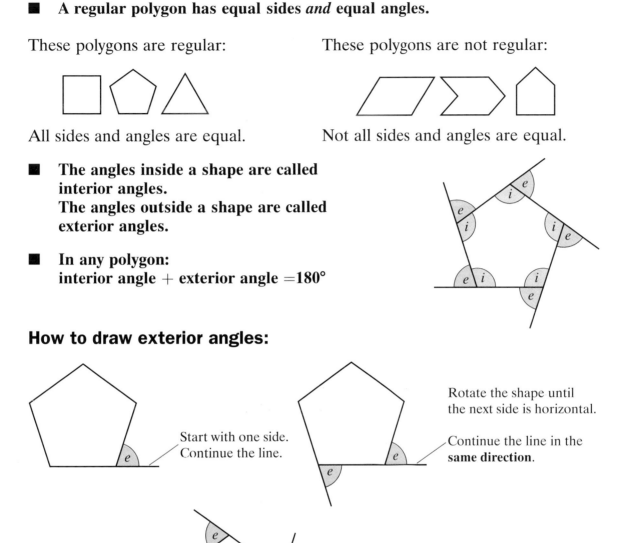

How to draw exterior angles:

Start with one side.
Continue the line.

Rotate the shape until the next side is horizontal.

Continue the line in the **same direction**.

Repeat until you have continued all the lines.

Your shape should now look like a Catherine wheel.

Measure all the exterior angles and add them together.
You should find that:

■   **The sum of the exterior angles of a polygon is 360°**

Example 12

Find the size of each interior angle in a regular hexagon.

There are two methods you can use.

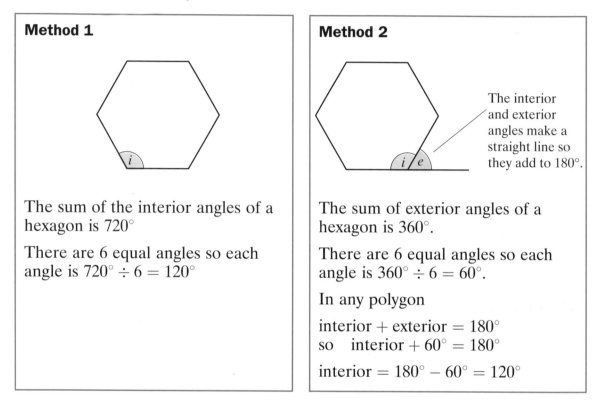

Method 1

The sum of the interior angles of a hexagon is 720°

There are 6 equal angles so each angle is 720° ÷ 6 = 120°

Method 2

The interior and exterior angles make a straight line so they add to 180°.

The sum of exterior angles of a hexagon is 360°.

There are 6 equal angles so each angle is 360° ÷ 6 = 60°.

In any polygon

interior + exterior = 180°
so   interior + 60° = 180°

interior = 180° − 60° = 120°

Exercise 2M

1   For each regular polygon find:
   • the size of an interior angle
   • the size of an exterior angle.

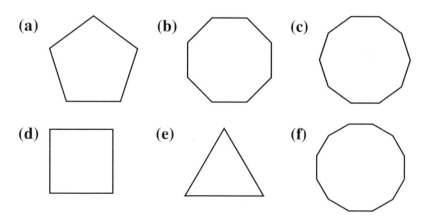

(a)   **(b)**   **(c)**

(d)   **(e)**   **(f)**

2 Find the missing angles:

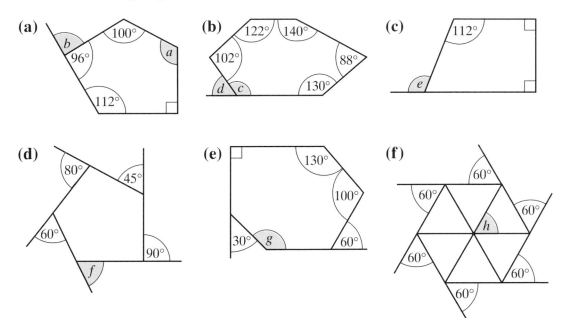

Summary of key points

1 A shape has rotational symmetry if it looks exactly the same after a rotation.

2 The order of rotational symmetry is the number of times it looks exactly the same in a full turn.

3 An angle is a measure of turn. It is usually measured in degrees (° for short).

4 Angles less than 90° are called acute angles.

5 Angles greater than 90° but less than 180° are called obtuse angles.

6 Angles greater than 180° are called reflex angles.

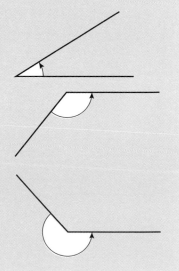

7   Angles on a corner add to 90°.

8   Angles on a straight line add to 180°.

9   Angles at a point add to 360°.

10 When two straight lines cross the opposite angles are equal.

11 The angles of a triangle add to 180°.

12 The angles of a quadrilateral add to 360°.

13 A regular polygon has equal sides *and* equal angles.

14 The angles inside a shape are called interior angles.
    The angles outside a shape are called exterior angles.
    In any polygon: interior angle + exterior angle =180°.

15 The sum of the exterior angles of a polygon is 360°.

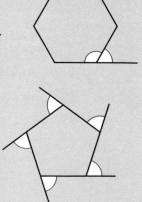

3 Multiplication and division

3.1 Multiplication and division up to 10 × 10

You will not always have a calculator with you so you need to learn your multiplication tables up to 10 × 10.

These exercises will help you.

25 ÷ 4 is 6 remainder 1 so they will pay just over £6 each.

Exercise 3A

1 Complete this 2 by 2 multiplication square. The first entry is filled in to show you how.

×	2	8
3		
5	10	

5 × 2 = 10 so write 10 in here.

2 This diagram shows a 3 by 3 multiplication square.
   (a) Find the missing numbers.
   (b) Make up your own square and try it on a friend.

×	5		
4		28	
		42	
9			72

3 For each multiplication square:
   • Complete the square
   • Find the total of the answers

(a)

×	3	5
2		
4		

(b)

×	3	6
2		
5		

(c) Do the same for some other 2 by 2 multiplication squares.
What do you notice about your results?

(d) Make up a 2 by 2 multiplication square for which the total of the answers is:
(i) 35 **(ii)** 42 **(iii)** 56 **(iv)** 72.

(e) Make up a 3 by 3 multiplication for which the total of the nine answers is **(i)** 64 **(ii)** 81 **(iii)** 100.

4 **(a)** Write down any pair of numbers that add up to 12. Multiply the numbers together.

$4 + 8 = 12$
$4 \times 8 = 32$

Do the same for other pairs of numbers that add up to 12.

Which pair of numbers gives the largest answer when you multiply them together?

$3 + 9 = 12$
$3 \times 9 = 27$

(b) Do the same for some other numbers which are less than 20.

(c) What do you notice?

5 Choose four numbers and write them in a 2×2 grid. For example 2, 4, 7 and 8.
Multiply the numbers on each side of the grid and add the answers.

$$8 + 32 + 56 + 14 = 110$$

Change the position of the four numbers in the grid and do the same again:

$$14 + 28 + 32 + 16 = 90$$

$2 \times 4 = 8$

2	4
7	8

$2 \times 7 = 14$ $4 \times 8 = 32$

$7 \times 8 = 56$

$2 \times 7 = 14$

2	7
8	4

$2 \times 8 = 16$ $7 \times 4 = 28$

$8 \times 4 = 32$

Try other positions of the four numbers in the grid.
What is the biggest total you can make?

Do the same for other sets of four numbers.
What do you notice?

6 Choose three consecutive numbers, for example 5, 6 and 7.

Consecutive means one after the other without gaps.

Multiply the two end numbers together $5 \times 7 = 35$
Multiply the middle number by itself $6 \times 6 = 36$

Do the same with other sets of three consecutive numbers.
Try to explain what you notice.

7   Find the missing numbers from each box:

(a)

$24 \div \square$

$16 \div \square \quad \langle\ 4\ \rangle \quad \square \div 9$

$32 \div \square$

(b)

$42 \div \square$

$36 \div \square \quad \langle\ 6\ \rangle \quad \square \div 8$

$\square \div 9$

The number in the middle is the result of each calculation for example:

$42 \div \boxed{7} = 6$

(c)

$35 \div \square$

$45 \div \square \quad \langle\ 5\ \rangle \quad \square \div 8$

$\square \div 6$

(d)

$81 \div \square$

$45 \div \square \quad \langle\ 9\ \rangle \quad 54 \div \square$

$\square \div 7$

(e)

$63 \div \square$

$56 \div \square \quad \langle\ 7\ \rangle \quad \square \div 6$

$\square \div 7$

(f)

$40 \div \square$

$\square \div 3 \quad \langle\ 8\ \rangle \quad \square \div 9$

$64 \div \square$

8   (a)   Fit the numbers 9, 9, 6, 6, 3, 3, 3, 2 into the grid to make the division sums correct.

(b)   Make up a question like this of your own. Hint: try putting 32 or 48 in the top left corner.

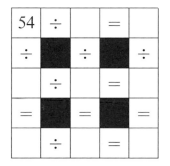

9   To complete the grid:
- Multiply a pair of numbers.
- Divide the answer by 7
- Write the remainder on the grid.

(a)   What do you notice?

(b)   Investigate this idea further.

$4 \times 5 = 20$

$20 \div 7 = 2$ remainder 6

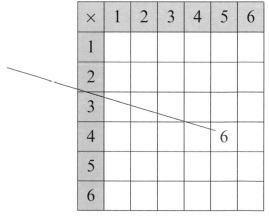

3.2 Using multiplication up to 10 × 10

Example 1

Warwick bought nine CDs in a charity shop for £3 each.
How much did he pay in total?

Write your answer out like this:

Total cost = £3 × 9

= £27

Example 2

Heather wants to buy a cream cake for each person in
her office. The cakes are in packs of 4 and there are
21 people in her office. How many packs of cakes
must she buy?

$21 \div 4 = 5$ remainder 1

If she buys 5 packs then one person will not get a
cake so she must buy 6 packs.

Example 3

Milly has to put 50 tulips into bunches of 6.
How many bunches can she make?

$50 \div 6 = 8$ remainder 2

She can make 8 bunches and has 2 tulips left over.

$8 \times 6 = 48$
$50 - 48 = 2$
so
$50 \div 6 = 8$
remainder 2

Exercise 3B

1   Fiona is arranging mini-cabs to take 27 people to a
    night club.
    Each cab can take 4 people.
    How many should she order?

2   Chloe jogs 9 miles every day.
    How many miles does she jog in a week?

3   A fruit grower is putting pears into packs.
    She has 60 pears and each pack holds 8.
    How many packs can she fill?

4   A group of 51 scouts are going camping.
Each tent sleeps 6 people.
How many tents will they need?

5   Michael bought six packs of socks.
Each pack contained four pairs of socks and the total
cost was £54.

(a) How many pairs of socks did he buy?
(b) How much did each pack of socks cost?

6   Every day Reiss does the following exercises:

   9 press-ups
   7 star jumps
   8 sit-ups
   6 stretches

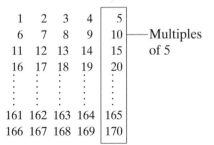

How many of each exercise does he do in a week?

3.3 Multiples

■ **The multiples of 5 are the answers
in the 5 times multiplication table:
5, 10, 15, 20, 25, . . . 165, 170 . . .**

$1 \times 5 =$ 5
$2 \times 5 =$ 10 — These are the
$3 \times 5 =$ 15   multiples of 5.
$4 \times 5 =$ 20
......
......
$33 \times 5 =$ 165 — $33 \times 5 = 165$ so 165
$34 \times 5 =$ 170   is a multiple of 5.

You can also find multiples of 5 by
writing counting numbers in rows of 5.

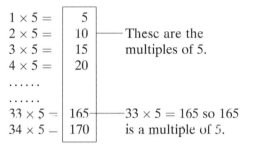

```
  1    2    3    4  │  5
  6    7    8    9  │ 10  ── Multiples
 11   12   13   14  │ 15        of 5
 16   17   18   19  │ 20
  :    :    :    :  │  :
  :    :    :    :  │  :
161  162  163  164  │165
166  167  168  169  │170
```

■ **The multiples of 2 are called the even numbers:
2, 4, 6, 8, 10, 12, . . .
The units digit of an even number is always
0, 2, 4, 6 or 8.**

■ **The other whole numbers are called odd numbers:
1, 3, 5, 7, 9, 11, 13, . . .
The units digit of an odd number is always
1, 3, 5, 7 or 9.**

Example 4

Which multiples of 7 lie between 30 and 50?

Write out the 7 times multiplication table. ⎯⎯⎯
The multiples of 7 between 30 and 50 are
35, 42 and 49.

$1 \times 7 = 7$
$2 \times 7 = 14$
$3 \times 7 = 21$
$4 \times 7 = 28$
$5 \times 7 = 35$
$6 \times 7 = 42$
$7 \times 7 = 49$
$7 \times 8 = 56$

Exercise 3C

1 Write down the first twenty even numbers.

2 Write down all the even numbers between 41 and 51.

3 What is the next even number after:
   (a) 35 **(b)** 63 **(c)** 91 **(d)** 137 **(e)** 109 **(f)** 283

4 Write down all the odd numbers between 40 and 50.

5 What is the next odd number after:
   (a) 62 **(b)** 38 **(c)** 56
   (d) 174 **(e)** 290 **(f)** 508

Remember:
EVEN numbers end
in 0, 2, 4, 6 and 8
ODD numbers end
in 1, 3, 5, 7 or 9

6 Write down the first five multiples of 7.

7 Write down the first five multiples of 6.

8 These numbers are multiples ⎯⎯⎯
of four: 140, 144, 148, 152.
What are the next two multiples
of four?

			140
141	142	143	144
145	146	147	148
149	150	151	152
153			?
			?

9 Which multiples of 8 are between
40 and 60?

10 Which multiples of 9 are between
20 and 50?

11 Which of these numbers are multiples
of 8?
   (a) 30 **(b)** 64 **(c)** 32
   (d) 46 **(e)** 28 **(f)** 40

12 Which of these numbers are multiples of 9?
   (a) 72 **(b)** 36 **(c)** 40 **(d)** 62 **(e)** 45 **(f)** 54

13 The number 6 can be placed in the table as shown because:

> It is a multiple of 3.
> It is not a multiple of 5.

(a) Place the rest of the numbers from 5 to 20 in the table.

(b) Make up a puzzle like this of your own.

	Multiple of 5	Not a multiple of 5	Less than 13	Greater than 13
Multiple of 3		6		
Not a multiple of 3				
Even number				
Odd number				

3.4 Factors

◼ **The factors of a number are the numbers that divide into it with no remainder.**
For example 1, 2, 5 and 10 are the factors of 10.
Factors are always whole numbers.

You can think of factors in several ways:

$1 \times 1 = 1$ $1 \times 2 = 2$ $1 \times 5 = 5$ **$1 \times 10 = 10$** $2 \times 1 = 2$ $2 \times 2 = 4$ **$2 \times 5 = 10$** $3 \times 1 = 3$ $3 \times 2 = 6$ $4 \times 1 = 4$ $4 \times 2 = 8$ $5 \times 1 = 5$ **$5 \times 2 = 10$** $6 \times 1 = 6$ $7 \times 1 = 7$ $8 \times 1 = 8$ $9 \times 1 = 9$ **$10 \times 1 = 10$**	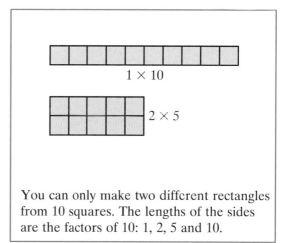
Ten appears as an answer in the multiplication tables for 1, 2, 5 and 10. It does not appear as an answer in any other tables.	You can only make two different rectangles from 10 squares. The lengths of the sides are the factors of 10: 1, 2, 5 and 10.

Example 5

Are 3 and 7 factors of 15?

15 divided by 3 = 5 remainder 0 so 3 is a factor of 15.
15 divided by 7 = 2 remainder 1 so 7 is not a factor of 15.

From the diagram you can see that the factors of 15 are 1, 3, 5 and 15.

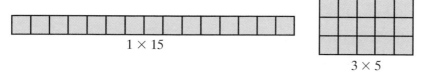

Example 6

Find all the factors of 8.

Draw all the rectangles you can make from 8 squares:

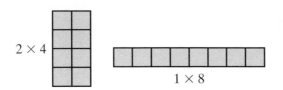

2×4 1×8

The lengths of the sides give the factors of 8: 1, 2, 4 and 8.

Exercise 3D

1   Write down all the factors of these numbers:
    (a) 16   (b) 12   (c) 18   (d) 24   (e) 21   (f) 15
    (g) 32   (h) 36   (i) 40   (j) 39   (k) 50   (l) 100

2   True or false?
    (a) 3 is a factor of 21   (b) 5 is a factor of 25
    (c) 7 is a factor of 24   (d) 9 is a factor of 54
    (e) 8 is a factor of 72   (f) 7 is a factor of 47
    (g) 5 is a factor of 45   (h) 8 is a factor of 36
    (i) 9 is a factor of 36   (j) 6 is a factor of 48

3   (a) Choose any two digits from the cloud.
         Find all the factors of each 2-digit number that you
         can make.

    4   3
    2   6

    (b) Which of the 2-digit numbers that you can make
         from the cloud has the greatest number of factors?

4   (a) Which is the first number to have:
         (i) 1 factor   (ii) 2 factors   (iii) 3 factors?
    (b) Investigate this idea further.

3.5 Prime numbers

■ **A number that has exactly two factors is a prime number. The factors are the number itself and 1.**

2, 3, 5, 7, 11, 13, 17, 19, 23, ... are all prime numbers.

1, 4, 6, 8, 9, 10, 12, 14, 15, ... are not prime numbers.

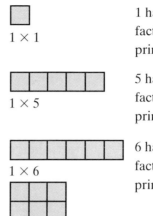

1 × 1

1 × 5

1 × 6

2 × 3

1 has only one factor. It is not a prime number.

5 has exactly two factors. It is a prime number.

6 has four factors. It is not a prime number.

There is no pattern to the prime numbers and they go on forever. After 2, all prime numbers are odd numbers (but not all odd numbers are prime numbers!).

Exercise 3E

1 **Activity** You will need a hundred square.
On your hundred square:

- Cross out 1 because it is not a prime number.
- Circle 2 and cross out all the other multiples of 2.
- Circle the next number that is not crossed out and cross out all of its multiples.
- Continue like this until you cannot circle any more numbers.

You circle 2 because it is prime. Any multiple of 2 cannot be prime.

This method is called the sieve of Eratosthenes.

Your hundred square will end up like this.
All the circled numbers are prime numbers.

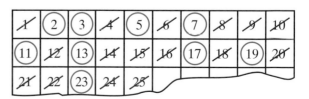

2 Find two prime numbers that add up to:
   (a) 8   (b) 10   (c) 12   (d) 14
   (e) 21   (f) 28   (g) 32   (h) 33

3   2 and 5 are a pair of prime numbers.
2 + 5 = 7 is a prime number.
Find other pairs of prime numbers whose total is a
prime number.
What do you notice about your answers?

4   Find three prime numbers whose total is a prime number.

5   The number 12 can be written as prime numbers $12 = 2 \times 2 \times 3$
multiplied together. Write each of these numbers as
prime numbers multiplied together:

   (a) 15   **(b)** 18   **(c)** 16   **(d)** 21
   (e) 25   **(f)** 28   **(g)** 30   **(h)** 35

6   Can all whole numbers be written as prime numbers
multiplied together?

3.6 Square numbers and square roots

You can arrange 16 square tiles to   ... but you can't arrange 6 square
make a square ...   tiles to make a square.

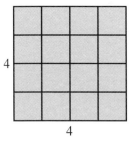   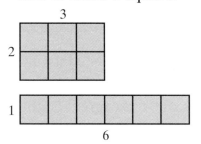

$16 = 4 \times 4 = 4^2$ (or four **squared**).
For this reason 16 is called a **square number**.
Because $16 = 4 \times 4$, 4 is called the **square root** of 16.

■   **A whole number multiplied by itself always gives a
square number.**

$1 \times 1 = 1$, $2 \times 2 = 4$, $3 \times 3 = 9$, $4 \times 4 = 16$, $5 \times 5 = 25$, ...

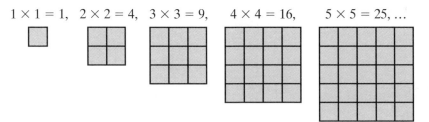

■   **1, 4, 9, 16, 25, ... are square numbers.**

■ **1 is called the square root of 1,**
2 is the square root of 4,
3 is the square root of 9, and so on ...

Hint:
You write $\sqrt{9} = 3$
which means 'the
square root of 9 is 3.

Exercise 3F

1   Make a list of the first thirty square numbers.

2   What is the square root of:
   (a) 36   **(b)** 64   **(c)** 81   **(d)** 121
   (e) 144   **(f)** 169   **(g)** 225   **(h)** 289
   (i) 400   **(j)** 441   **(k)** 729   **(l)** 900

3   You can write 12 as the difference of two square numbers.
   You can write 13 as the sum of two square numbers.
   Which numbers up to 20 can be written as either the difference or the sum of two square numbers?

$12 = 16 - 4$
$13 = 9 + 4$

4   Which prime numbers less than 100 can be written as the sum of two square numbers?

$73 \quad = \quad 9 \quad + \quad 64$
prime   square   square

5   **Activity**
   (a) How many cubes do you need to build each of the double-sided staircases shown?

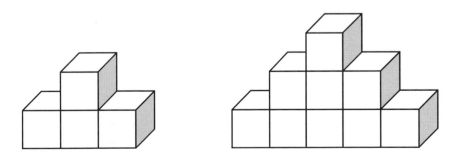

   (b) Investigate how many cubes you need to build other double-sided staircases. Try to explain anything you discover.

   (c) What is the tallest double-sided staircase you can build using:
      (i)   50 cubes   **(ii)**   200 cubes
      (iii) 500 cubes   **(iv)** 1000 cubes?

3.7 Multiplying 2- and 3-digit numbers by a 1-digit number

There is an easy way to do multiplications such as 37×4:

Think of 37 as $30 + 7$

You know that:
$$30 \times 4 = 120$$
$$7 \times 4 = \underline{\quad 28} +$$
So $\quad 37 \times 4 = \overline{148}$

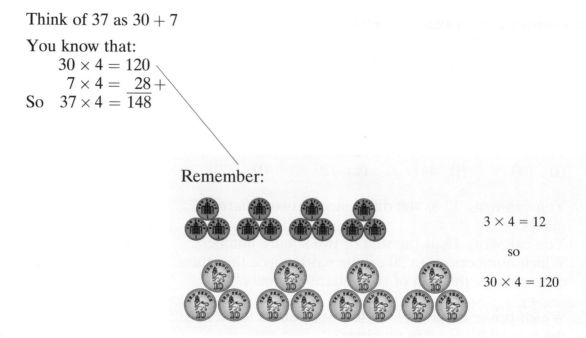

Remember:

$3 \times 4 = 12$

so

$30 \times 4 = 120$

You can set the working out like this:

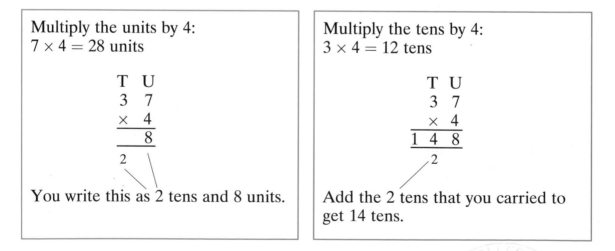

Multiply the units by 4: $7 \times 4 = 28$ units	Multiply the tens by 4: $3 \times 4 = 12$ tens
$$\begin{array}{cc} T & U \\ 3 & 7 \\ \times & 4 \\ \hline & 8 \\ 2 & \end{array}$$	$$\begin{array}{ccc} T & U \\ 3 & 7 \\ \times & 4 \\ \hline 1\ 4 & 8 \\ 2 & \end{array}$$
You write this as 2 tens and 8 units.	Add the 2 tens that you carried to get 14 tens.

You can use the same method to multiply any number by a 1-digit number.

Example 7

To work out 468×7 you multiply
the hundreds, tens and units
by 7 in turn, then add each answer:

$$400 \times 7 = 2800$$
$$60 \times 7 = 420$$
$$8 \times 7 = \underline{56} +$$
$$3276$$

You can also set it out like this:

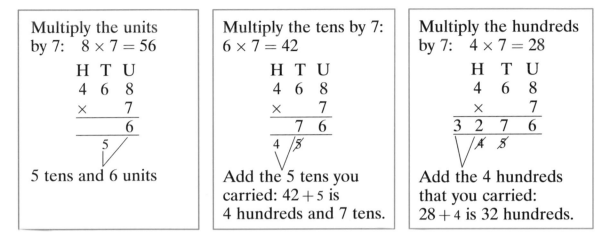

Multiply the units by 7: $8 \times 7 = 56$	Multiply the tens by 7: $6 \times 7 = 42$	Multiply the hundreds by 7: $4 \times 7 = 28$
H T U 4 6 8 × 7 ⎯⎯⎯ 6 5	H T U 4 6 8 × 7 ⎯⎯⎯ 7 6 4 5	H T U 4 6 8 × 7 ⎯⎯⎯⎯ 3 2 7 6 4 5
5 tens and 6 units	Add the 5 tens you carried: $42 + 5$ is 4 hundreds and 7 tens.	Add the 4 hundreds that you carried: $28 + 4$ is 32 hundreds.

Exercise 3G

Work out:

1
(a) 24×6 (b) 63×7 (c) 47×2 (d) 38×9
(e) 75×3 (f) 94×5 (g) 37×8 (h) 54×8
(i) 53×6 (j) 29×9 (k) 84×4 (l) 73×9

2
(a) 213×4 (b) 423×3 (c) 624×6 (d) 495×6
(e) 429×6 (f) 375×3 (g) 733×5 (h) 386×6
(i) 978×7 (j) 788×8 (k) 295×4 (l) 989×9

3.8 Multiplying by 10 and 100

Multiplying whole numbers by 10 is easy.

To multiply 24×10:
$$20 \times 10 = 200$$
$$4 \times 10 = \underline{40} +$$
So $24 \times 10 = 240$

■ **To multiply a whole number by 10 move each digit one column to the left and put 0 in the units column.**

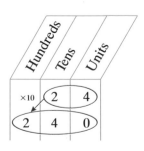

There is also a quick way to multiply whole numbers by 100.

As $100 = 10 \times 10$ you can just multiply by 10 twice:

$$24 \times 100 = 24 \times 10 \times 10$$
$$- 240 \times 10$$
$$= 2400$$

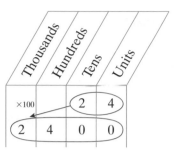

■   **To multiply a whole number by 100 move each digit two columns to the left and put 0 in the tens and units columns.**

Example 8

Work out $560 \div 10$

Dividing is the opposite of multiplying so you remove the 0 and move the digits one place to the right.

$$560 \div 10 = 56$$

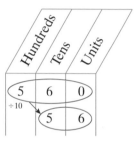

Exercise 3H

Work out:

1   (a) 53×10 (b) 38×10 (c) 49×100
   (d) 87×10 (e) 10×62 (f) 100×32
   (g) 254×10 (h) 132×100 (i) 10×187
   (j) 100×76 (k) 97×100 (l) 100×10

2   (a) $34 \times 10 \times 10$ (b) $87 \times 10 \times 100$
   (c) $4 \times 8 \times 100$ (d) $456 \times 100 \times 10$
   (e) $9 \times 7 \times 10 \times 10$ (f) 100×100
   (g) $10 \times 100 \times 10$ (h) $100 \times 34 \times 10$ Hint: think of this as
   (i) $10 \times 628 \times 100$ (j) $4 \times 100 \times 8$ ———— $4 \times 8 \times 100$

3   (a) $360 \div 10$ (b) $780 \div 10$
   (c) $9800 \div 100$ (d) $6500 \div 100$
   (e) $7800 \div 10$ (f) $8400 \div 10$
   (g) $65\,000 \div 100$ (h) $8000 \div 100$
   (i) $65\,000 \div 10$ (j) $506\,000 \div 100$

Example 9

Find 64×80

You can think of 80 as 8×10, so:

$$64 \times 80 = 64 \times 8 \times 10$$
$$= 512 \times 10$$
$$= 5120$$

$$\begin{array}{r} 6\,4 \\ \times\,8 \\ \hline 5\,1\,2 \\ {\scriptstyle 3} \end{array}$$

■ **To multiply by 80, multiply by 8 then multiply by 10.**
■ **To multiply by 800, multiply by 8 then multiply by 100.**

Exercise 3I

Find:

1   **(a)** 23×30 **(b)** 47×20 **(c)** 38×30
    (d) 63×40 **(e)** 83×40 **(f)** 70×56 ——— Hint: think of this as 56×70
    (g) 60×48 **(h)** 90×63 **(i)** 37×40
    (j) 49×50 **(k)** 90×72 **(l)** 39×60

2   **(a)** 24×200 **(b)** 36×300 **(c)** 74×600
    (d) 38×500 **(e)** 400×85 **(f)** 600×48
    (g) 39×200 **(h)** 58×700 **(i)** 900×84
    (j) 74×700 **(k)** 800×72 **(l)** 99×900

3   **(a)** 253×20 **(b)** 463×40 **(c)** 764×80
    (d) 962×60 **(e)** 654×300 **(f)** 432×400
    (g) 352×800 **(h)** 745×90 **(i)** 877×40
    (j) 408×70 **(k)** 490×40 **(l)** 600×30

3.9 Multiplying 2- or 3-digit numbers by a 2-digit number

You sometimes need to be able to do harder multiplications without a calculator. This section shows you an easy way to do harder multiplications on paper.

Example 10

Work out 694×74.

Think of 74 as $70 + 4$, so:

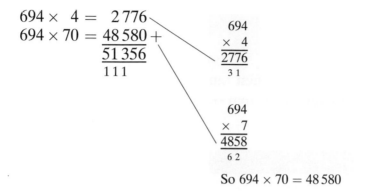

$$694 \times 4 = 2776$$
$$694 \times 70 = 48\,580 +$$
$$\overline{51\,356}$$
$$\underline{1\,1\,1}$$

$$\begin{array}{r} 694 \\ \times\ \ 4 \\ \hline 2776 \\ \underline{3\ 1} \end{array}$$

$$\begin{array}{r} 694 \\ \times\ \ 7 \\ \hline 4858 \\ \underline{6\ 2} \end{array}$$

So $694 \times 70 = 48\,580$

You can set this out as:

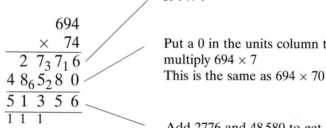

694×4

$$\begin{array}{r} 694 \\ \times\ \ 74 \\ \hline 2\ 7_3 7_1 6 \\ 4\ 8_6 5_2 8\ 0 \\ \hline 5\ 1\ 3\ 5\ 6 \\ \underline{1\ 1\ 1} \end{array}$$

Put a 0 in the units column then
multiply 694×7
This is the same as 694×70

Add 2776 and 48 580 to get 694×74

Exercise 3J

1   Work out:
   (a) 43×21 **(b)** 76×32 **(c)** 89×43 **(d)** 673×28
   (e) 492×67 **(f)** 388×65 **(g)** 306×84 **(h)** 460×29
   (i) 738×92 **(j)** 88×44 **(k)** 464×71 **(l)** 888×88

2   **(a)** Write any four digits as a 2-digit × 2-digit
      multiplication and work out the answer.
      Try other arrangements for your four digits.
      Which arrangement gives the largest answer?
      Which arrangement gives the smallest answer?

   (b) Repeat part **(a)** but choose 5 digits and make a
      3-digit × 2-digit multiplication.

For example, choose
4, 9, 3 and 6:

$$\begin{array}{r} 46 \\ \times\ \ 93 \\ \hline 1\ 3_1 8 \\ 41_5 4\ 0 \\ \hline 42\ 7\ 8 \end{array}$$

3.10 Dividing 3-digit numbers by 1- or 2-digit numbers

Divisions are easy to do with pencil and paper.
To work out $785 \div 4$, set it out like this:

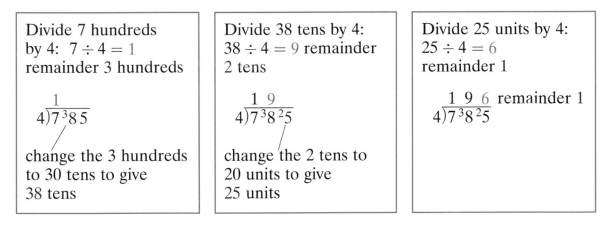

Divide 7 hundreds
by 4: $7 \div 4 = 1$
remainder 3 hundreds

$$\frac{1}{4)7\,{}^3 8\,5}$$

change the 3 hundreds
to 30 tens to give
38 tens

Divide 38 tens by 4:
$38 \div 4 = 9$ remainder
2 tens

$$\frac{1\ 9}{4)7\,{}^3 8\,{}^2 5}$$

change the 2 tens to
20 units to give
25 units

Divide 25 units by 4:
$25 \div 4 = 6$
remainder 1

$$\frac{1\ 9\ 6}{4)7\,{}^3 8\,{}^2 5} \text{ remainder 1}$$

So $785 \div 4 = 196$ remainder 1.

Example 11

Calculate $87 \div 5$
$8 \div 5 = 1$ remainder 3
$37 \div 5 = 7$ remainder 2

$$\frac{1\ 7}{5)8\,{}^3 7} \text{ remainder 2}$$

Exercise 3K

Calculate:

1   (a) $95 \div 4$
    (c) $97 \div 4$
    (e) $78 \div 5$
    (g) $798 \div 7$
    (i) $825 \div 5$
    (k) $938 \div 8$

    (b) $85 \div 6$
    (d) $947 \div 4$
    (f) $867 \div 6$
    (h) $944 \div 8$
    (j) $89 \div 3$
    (l) $653 \div 5$

2   (a) $467 \div 3$
    (c) $479 \div 4$
    (e) $407 \div 6$
    (g) $203 \div 3$
    (i) $507 \div 7$
    (k) $753 \div 9$

    (b) $637 \div 7$
    (d) $296 \div 4$
    (f) $999 \div 8$
    (h) $400 \div 7$
    (j) $111 \div 6$
    (l) $748 \div 7$

Example 12

Work out $864 \div 23$.

You can't divide the hundreds by 23 so do 86 tens $\div$ 23:

Bring down the 4 units and work out 174 units $\div$ 23:

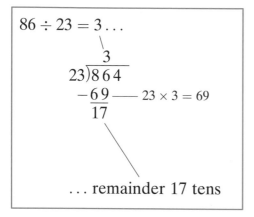

$86 \div 23 = 3 \ldots$

$$\begin{array}{r} 3 \\ 23\overline{)864} \\ -69 \\ \hline 17 \end{array}$$

$23 \times 3 = 69$

$\ldots$ remainder 17 tens

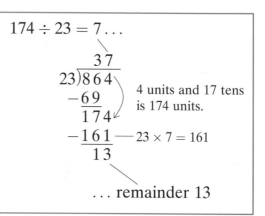

$174 \div 23 = 7 \ldots$

$$\begin{array}{r} 37 \\ 23\overline{)864} \\ -69 \\ \hline 174 \\ -161 \\ \hline 13 \end{array}$$

4 units and 17 tens is 174 units.

$23 \times 7 = 161$

$\ldots$ remainder 13

So $864 \div 23 = 37$ remainder 13.

Exercise 3L

1 (a) $897 \div 21$ (b) $896 \div 26$ (c) $956 \div 42$ (d) $869 \div 36$
(e) $786 \div 56$ (f) $694 \div 17$ (g) $592 \div 18$ (h) $982 \div 67$
(i) $675 \div 31$ (j) $497 \div 16$ (k) $381 \div 23$ (l) $746 \div 19$

For questions **2 – 7** you must decide whether to use multiplication or division to solve the problem.

2 A shop ordered 23 video recorders at £258 each. What was the total cost of the video recorders?

3 Ray's car uses a litre of petrol every 18 kilometres it travels. How many litres will he need to travel 850 kilometres?

4 (a) There are 36 packets of crisps in a box. Each packet costs 28p. What is the total cost of a box of crisps?

(b) A school tuck shop sells they 900 packets of crisps a week. How many boxes should they order each week?

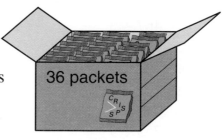

36 packets

5   Danielle buys a television.
    She pays 24 monthly instalments of £19.
    How much does she pay in total?

6   A cinema has 38 rows of 46 seats.
    How many seats are there in the cinema?

7   How many 55 seat coaches would be needed to take
    857 people on a trip?

3.11 Powers of numbers

Astronomers often have to deal with very large distances.

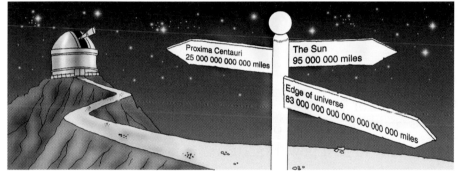

They write numbers a special way to make their
calculations easier:

	You write:	You say:
$10 \times 10 = 100$	10^2	'10 to the power 2'
$10 \times 10 \times 10 = 1000$	10^3	'10 to the power 3'
$10 \times 10 \times 10 \times 10 = 10\,000$	10^4	'10 to the power 4'

... and so on.

You can write any number as a power:

■ $3^5 = 3 \times 3 \times 3 \times 3 \times 3$. **You say '3 to the power of 5'.**

You can use powers to write large numbers in a shorter
form:

distance to the Sun
$= 95\,000\,000$ miles
$= 95 \times 1\,000\,000$ miles
$= 95 \times 10^6$ miles 10^{12} — twelve is the **power** or **index**.

distance to Proxima Centauri (the nearest star)
$= 25\,000\,000\,000\,000$ miles
$= 25 \times 10^{12}$ miles

distance to the edge of the Universe $= 83\,000\,000\,000\,000\,000\,000\,000$ miles
$= 83 \times 10^{21}$ miles

Example 13

Write $6 \times 6 \times 6 \times 6 \times 6$ as a power of 6.
$6 \times 6 \times 6 \times 6 \times 6 = 6^5$

Example 14

Write 625 as a power of 5.
$625 = 5 \times 5 \times 5 \times 5 = 5^4$

Example 15

Write 10 000 000 as a power of 10.
There are seven zeros after the 1
So $10\,000\,000 = 10^7$

Example 16

Work out 8^3.
$8^3 = 8 \times 8 \times 8 = 512$

Exercise 3M

1 Write:
  (a) $2 \times 2 \times 2 \times 2$ as a power of 2
  (b) $7 \times 7 \times 7$ as a power of 7
  (c) $3 \times 3 \times 3 \times 3 \times 3 \times 3$ as a power of 3
  (d) $10 \times 10 \times 10 \times 10 \times 10$ as a power of 10
  (e) 9×9 as a power of 9
  (f) $4 \times 4 \times 4 \times 4 \times 4 \times 4 \times 4$ as a power of 4

2 Work out:
  (a) 5 squared
  (b) 2 cubed
  (c) 4 squared
  (d) 5 cubed
  (e) 3 cubed
  (f) 10 squared
  (g) 10 cubed
  (h) 6 squared
  (i) 7 squared
  (j) 100 squared
  (k) 1 squared
  (l) 1 cubed

Hint:
'5 squared' means 5^2.
'5 cubed' means 5^3.

3 Work out:
  (a) 2^4
  (b) 3^4
  (c) 10^5
  (d) 5^5
  (e) 4^3
  (f) 1^6
  (g) 8^2
  (h) 0^6
  (i) 9^3
  (j) 100^3
  (k) 6^3
  (l) 7^3

4 Write:
  (a) 16 as a power of 4
  (b) 36 as a power of 6
  (c) 27 as a power of 3
  (d) 10 000 as a power of 10
  (e) 32 as a power of 2
  (f) 64 as a power of 4
  (g) 81 as a power of 3
  (h) 125 as a power of 5

Summary of key points

1 The multiples of 5 are the answers in the 5 times multiplication table: 5, 10, 15, 20, 25, 30, 35, ...

2 The multiples of 2 are called the even numbers: 2, 4, 6, 8, 10, 12, ...
The units digit of an even number is always 0, 2, 4, 6 or 8.

3 The other whole numbers are called odd numbers: 1, 3, 5, 7, 9, 11, 13, ...
The units digit of an odd number is always 1, 3, 5, 7 or 9.

4 The factors of a number are the numbers that divide into it with no remainder.
For example 1, 2, 5 and 10 are the factors of 10.
Factors are always whole numbers.

5 A number that has exactly two factors is a prime number. These factors are the number itself and 1.

2, 3, 5, 7, 11, 13, 17, 19, 23, ...
are prime numbers.

1, 4, 6, 8, 9, 10, 12, 14, 15, ...
are not prime numbers.

6 A whole number multiplied by itself always gives a square number.
$1 \times 1 = 1, \quad 2 \times 2 = 4, \quad 3 \times 3 = 9, \quad 4 \times 4 = 16, \quad 5 \times 5 = 25, ...$

7 1, 4, 9, 16, 25, ... are called square numbers

8 1 is called the square root of 1
2 is the square root of 4
3 is the square root of 9, and so on ...

9 To multiply a whole number by 10 move each digit one column to the left and put 0 in the units column.

10 To multiply a whole number by 100 move each digit two columns to the left and put 0 in the tens and units columns.

11 To multiply by 80, multiply by 8 then multiply by 10.
To multiply by 800, multiply by 8 then multiply by 100.

12 10^2 means $10 \times 10 = 100$. You say '10 to the power of 2'.
10^3 means $10 \times 10 \times 10 = 1000$. You say '10 to the power of 3'.
10^4 means $10 \times 10 \times 10 \times 10 = 10\,000$. You say '10 to the power of 4'.
and so on . . .

13 10^2 is also called 10 squared.
10^3 is also called 10 cubed.

4 Working with algebra

Algebra is a part of maths which uses letters or symbols to represent numbers.

Scientists use algebra to help them study the motion of planets.

Example 1

Lucy has some scarves. How many has she got?
Using algebra you can say, 'Lucy has x scarves'.

If she buys two more scarves how many will she have altogether?

She has x scarves + 2 scarves.
Using algebra you can say that she has $x + 2$ scarves.

$x + 2$ is an algebraic expression – a way of describing something using algebra.

Example 2

Manisha has b posters. She sells 3 of them.
How many posters does she have left?

She has $b - 3$ posters left.

Example 3

Write a question which has the answer $p + 2$.

Mark has p books and Shania has 2 books.
How many books do they have altogether?

Exercise 4A

1 (a) Jessica has some photographs.
       Use algebra to say how many she has.

(b) A garage has some cars for sale.
  The owner has not counted the cars.
  Use algebra to say how many cars she has.

(c) Dora has x bottles and Bridgit has y bottles.
  How many bottles do they have altogether?

(d) Gianni has r sweets. He gives 8 sweets to his friend.
  How many sweets does Gianni have left?

(e) Daniel has a pens and Jane has 23 pens.
  How many pens do they have altogether?

(f) Alan has c crayons and Neil has 2 more crayons
  than Alan.
  How many crayons does Neil have?

(g) Martyn has y pencils. Debbie borrows 6 pencils.
  How many pencils does Martyn have left?

2 Make up a question like the ones above for each of
  these answers:

(a) $x + 2$ (b) $p + q$ (c) $a - b$
(d) $y + 5$ (e) $10 - s$ (f) $n - 12$

4.1 Collecting like terms

At Yo-Yo's Pizza's a standard cheese and tomato pizza
costs p pence. Extra toppings cost:

Topping:	Price
Tuna	t
Onions	o
Sweetcorn	s
Ham	h

Yo-Yo's Pizza's

Marino _____
Italiano _____
Meaty _____
New Yorker _____
Vegas ⓥ _____
Yo-Yo special _____

or choose your
own toppings!!

Example 4

One table orders these four pizzas:

Marino: Standard with extra tuna, onions and sweetcorn
Italiano: Plain tomato and cheese
Meaty: 2 extra ham toppings
New Yorker: One of each extra topping

(a) What is the cost of each pizza?
(b) What is the total cost?
(c) What is the difference in cost between the Meaty and Italiano pizzas?

(a) Marine: $p + t + o + s$

Italiano: p

Meaty: $p + h + h = p + 2h$

New Yorker: $p + t + o + s + h$

Hint:
Meaty is:
  standard $= p$
  $+2$ extra ham $= h + h$
So it costs $p + h + h$,
or $p + 2h$.

(b) Total cost $= p + t + o + s + p + p + 2h + p + t + o + s + h$

You can collect all of the same letters together:

$$\underbrace{p + p + p + p}_{} + \underbrace{t + t}_{} + \underbrace{o + o}_{} + \underbrace{s + s}_{} + \underbrace{h + 2h}_{}$$
$$= \quad 4p \quad + \quad 2t \quad + \quad 2o \quad + \quad 2s \quad + \quad 3h$$

Terms that use the same letter are called *like terms*.

(c) The difference in cost $= p + 2h - p$
$$= p - p + 2h$$
$$= 2h$$

Remember:
To find the difference you always subtract.

■ **Bringing terms together is called 'collecting like terms'.**
■ **Making an expression simpler is called simplifying.**

Example 5

Simplify:
(a) $8t - 3t$
(b) $10x + 2y - 4x + 2y$
(c) $3y + 2x$
(d) $3y + 9 + 5y - 3$

(a) $8t - 3t = 5t$
(b) $10x + 2y - 4x + 2y = 10x - 4x + 2y + 2y$
$$= 6x + 4y$$
(c) There are no like terms so the expression cannot be simplified.
(d) $3y + 9 + 5y - 3 = 3y + 5y + 9 - 3$
$$= 8y + 6$$

Exercise 4B

Simplify:

1   $4a + 4b + 4a + 4b$ 2 $6c + 4d + 4c + 6d$
3   $4r + 4r - 4r + 6r$ 4 $6y + 9x + 6y - 6x$
5   $6w + 10r + 4w + 6r$ 6 $10a - 6b - 4a - 8b$
7   $c + 6d + 6c - d$ 8 $4a + 10 + 6a + 8$

9 $10b - 5 - 3b + 9$

10 $6a + 4a - 4a + 8a$

11 $4r + 10r - 6a - 9r$

12 $6a + 4a - 6a + a$

13 $10r - 6r - 4r - r$

14 $4y + 6x + 6y - 6y - b$

15 $8q + 4 + 6q - q + 4$

16 $15p + 8d - 8m - 8d + 4$

17 $6m + 6q - 6m + 6q$

18 $10a + 4b + 6b + 10b + a$

19 $8r - 6r + 6r - 4r$

20 $6m - 4q - 4q + 6q$

21 $6m + 6d + 6d + m + d$

22 $8c + 4c - 4 + 6c + 4$

23 $e + 8d + 4c - 6d + c$

24 $15c + 10r - 6c - 6c + 4r$

25 $15a + 8b + 6a - 10a + b - 4a$

26 $6a + 6a - 4a + 6b - 4a + b$

27 $15a - 6b + 4a - 6b + 4$

28 $6a + 4 + 6a - 4 + 6a$

4.2 Multiplying terms together

Yo-Yo's Pizza introduce the new Roma pizza.

To work out how much dough they need they measure its area:

Remember:
Area = length × width

There is more about area on p. 218

Each slice is
a wide and b long

Here is the whole pizza:

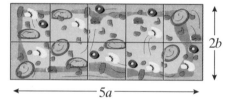

Area of pizza $= 5a \times 2b$

$$= 5 \times a \times 2 \times b$$

Simplify by collecting like terms

$$= 5 \times 2 \times a \times b$$

$$= 10ab$$

Hint:
$5a = 5 \times a$
$2b = 2 \times b$

You can use this method to simplify more complicated expressions:

Example 6

Simplify $7xy + 4z$

$$\text{Area} = 7xy \times 4z = 7 \times x \times y \times 4 \times z$$
$$= 7 \times 4 \times x \times y \times z$$
$$= 28xyz$$

Example 7

Simplify these expressions:

(a) $5s \times 3t$ **(b)** $7cd \times 5e$ **(c)** $10ab \times 3mn$

(a) $5 \times s \times 3 \times t = 5 \times 3 \times s \times t$
$$= 15st$$

(b) $7 \times c \times d \times 5 \times e = 7 \times 5 \times c \times d \times e$
$$= 35cde$$

(c) $10 \times a \times b \times 3 \times m \times n = 10 \times 3 \times a \times b \times m \times n$
$$= 30abmn$$

Exercise 4C

1 Work out the area of these pizzas:

(a)

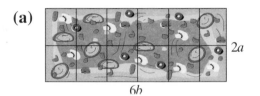

$2a$

$6b$

(b)

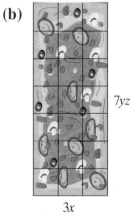

$7yz$

$3x$

(c)

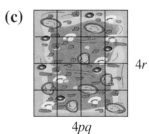

$4r$

$4pq$

2 Multiply the following:

  (a) $3z \times 6y$ **(b)** $4z \times 3y$

  (c) $6m \times 4n$ **(d)** $4c \times 4d$

  (e) $4p \times 5r$ **(f)** $m \times 3n$

  (g) $3c \times 4d$ **(h)** $6r \times 5s$

  (i) $6z \times 6y$ **(j)** $4zy \times 3m$

  (k) $3cd \times 4t$ **(l)** $6ab \times 4m$

  (m) $8mn \times 3e$ **(n)** $6p \times 3st$

  (o) $3mn \times 4efg$ **(p)** $2mn \times 5abc$

4.3 Brackets in algebra

Mark buys four Meaty pizzas.

The total cost is 4 lots of $p + 2h$:

$$p + 2h + p + 2h + p + 2h + p + 2h$$

Collect like terms:

$$= p + p + p + p \ + \ 2h + 2h + 2h + 2h$$

Add them together:

$$= 4p + 8h$$

or

$$4(p + 2h) = 4 \times p \ + \ 4 \times 2h$$

$$= 4p + 8h$$

Yo-Yo's Pizza's

Pizza	Price
Marino	$p + t + o + s$
Italiano	p
Meaty	$p + 2h$
New Yorker	$p + t + o + s + s$

Example 8

Chantel buys two Marino pizzas.
What is the total cost?

Total cost $= 2(p + t + o + s)$

$2(p + t + o + s)$

$$= 2 \times p \ + \ 2 \times t \ + \ 2 \times o \ + \ 2 \times s$$ — Multiply each term in the bracket
by the term outside the bracket.

$$= 2p + 2t + 2o + 2s$$

■ **Removing the brackets in an expression is called expanding the brackets.**

Example 9

Expand these expressions:

(a) $2(3x + 1)$
$= 2 \times 3x + 2 \times 1$
$= 6x + 2$

(b) $5(b - 2c)$
$= 5 \times b - 5 \times 2c$
$= 5b - 10c$

Exercise 4D

1   What is the cost for these pizza orders?
     Use the board at the top of the page to help you.
     (a) 2 Meaty pizzas   (b) 4 New Yorkers
     (c) 3 Italianos and 1 Marino   (d) 5 Marino and 2 Meaty

2 Expand:

(a) $3(2x - 3y)$ (b) $2(m - 2n)$
(c) $4(2x + 5y)$ (d) $3(3p + q)$
(e) $2(4x + 3y)$ (f) $8(2p + 3s)$
(g) $7(2p - 7q)$ (h) $5(3m + 7n)$
(i) $4(3r - 2s)$ (j) $2(2x + 3y - 2z)$
(k) $3(2p + 4q - 3r)$ (l) $2(a + b + c)$
(m) $4(2x - y + 5z)$ (n) $3(2a - 3b + 5c)$

4.4 Adding expressions with brackets

To simplify expressions like $2(3x + y) + 3(x + 5y)$ you need
to expand the brackets and then collect like terms.

Example 10

Simplify $2(3x + y) \ + \ 3(x + 5y)$

Expand the brackets:

$$2(3x \ + \ y) \ + \ 3(x \ + \ 5y)$$
$$= 2 \times 3x + 2 \times y \ + \ 3 \times x + 3 \times 5y$$
$$= \quad 6x \ + \ 2y \ + \ 3x \ + \ 15y$$

Simplify by
collecting like
terms:

$$= \qquad 9x \ + \ 17y$$

Exercise 4E

1 Expand the brackets in these expressions and then
collect like terms.

(a) $3(x + y) + 2(x + y)$ (b) $4(a + b) + 3(a + b)$
(c) $2(3x + y) + 2(2x + 3y)$ (d) $3(2a + b) + 4(a + b)$
(e) $3(4a + 3b) + 2(2a - 3c)$ (f) $4(p + q) + 2(2p - q)$
(g) $3(3c + 2d) + 5(c - d)$ (h) $5(p + q) + 6(2p + 3q)$
(i) $5(x - 2y) + 3(2x + 5y)$ (j) $3(4s - 5t) + 7(2s + 3t)$
(k) $3(x - y) + 3(x + y)$ (l) $2(3a + 4b) + 3(2a - 3b)$
(m) $8(3x - 2y) + 4(7x - 3y)$ (n) $4(3x - 2y) + 3(x - y)$
(o) $2(x + 3y) + 7(4x + 3y)$ (p) $7(3a + 5b) + 4(5a + 3b)$
(q) $5(2p + q) + 2(p - 3q)$ (r) $3(3x - 2y) + 4(2x - y)$
(s) $9(2a + b) + 2(a - 4b)$ (t) $4(e + 2f) + 3(e - f)$

4.5 Using powers in algebra

You can use powers to multiply two or more letters that are the same:

There is more about powers on p. 63

	You write:	You say:
$y \times y$	y^2	'y squared'
$y \times y \times y$	y^3	'y cubed'
$y \times y \times y \times y$	y^4	'y to the fourth' or 'y to the power 4'
$y \times y \times y \times y \times y$	y^5	'y to the fifth' or 'y to the power 5'

Example 11

Simplify:

(a) $t \times t \times t$

$t \times t \times t = t^3$

(b) $8 \times a \times a \times a \times a \times a$

$8 \times a \times a \times a \times a \times a = 8a^5$

Write without powers:

(a) b^6

$b^6 = b \times b \times b \times b \times b \times b$

(b) $10r^3$

$10r^3 = 10 \times r \times r \times r$

Exercise 4F

1 Simplify:

(a) $a \times a$
(b) $b \times b \times b$
(c) $c \times c \times c \times c$
(d) $x \times x \times x \times x$
(e) $y \times y \times y \times y \times y$
(f) $s \times s \times s \times s \times s \times s$
(g) $w \times w \times w$
(h) $z \times z$
(i) $p \times p \times p \times p \times p \times p$
(j) $4 \times m \times m \times m \times m$
(k) $5 \times t \times t \times t \times t \times t$
(l) $3 \times 2 \times c \times c \times c$
(m) $2 \times 2 \times a \times a \times a \times a$
(n) $7 \times 3 \times d \times d \times d \times d \times d \times d$

2 Write these expressions without using powers:
for example, x^2 can be written as $x \times x$

(a) x^2
(b) y^3
(c) 3^2
(d) t^4
(e) m^3
(f) n^5
(g) a^7
(h) b^5
(i) c^4
(j) d^8
(k) $4r^5$
(l) $5p^4$
(m) $2q^9$
(n) $3z^5$
(o) $12s^2$

Summary of key points

1 Bringing terms together is called 'collecting like terms'.

e.g. $3x + 5x = 8x$

2 Making an expression simpler is called simplifying.

e.g. $2a + 3b + 7a = 9a + 3b$

3 Removing the brackets in an expression is called expanding the brackets.

$$4(p + 2h) = 4p + 8h$$

5 Number patterns

Number patterns can produce images like these on a computer.

You will explore some number patterns in this chapter.

5.1 Patterns from dots and matchsticks

Here are the first four shapes in a dot pattern:

1 dot ...   4 dots ...   7 dots ...   10 dots ...

Using numbers the sequence is

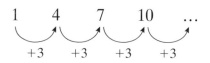

A **sequence** is another name for a number pattern.

The rule to go from one shape to the next is **'add 3'**.

Here are the first four shapes in a matchstick pattern:

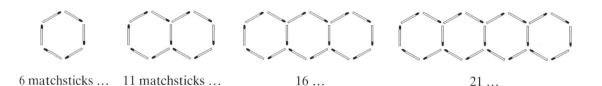

6 matchsticks ...   11 matchsticks ...   16 ...   21 ...

The number pattern or sequence is:

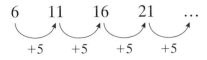

6   11   16   21   ...

  +5   +5   +5   +5

Exercise 5A

1 Copy these patterns.
For each pattern draw the next two shapes.

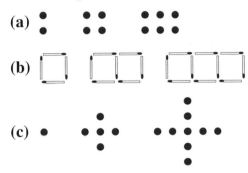

(a)

(b)

(c)

2 In the shape patterns below:
- write down the number sequence, filling in the missing numbers
- write down the rule to go from one shape to the next.

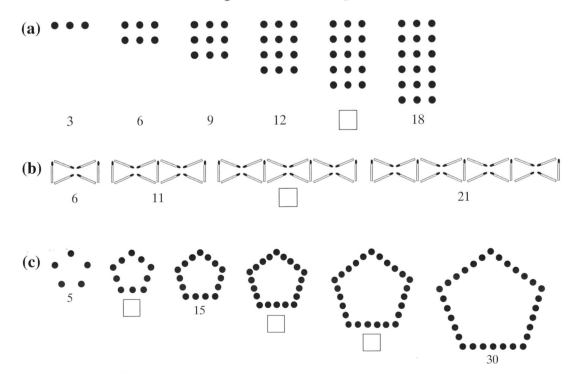

(a)   3   6   9   12   ☐   18

(b)   6   11   ☐   21

(c)   5   ☐   15   ☐   ☐   30

(d)

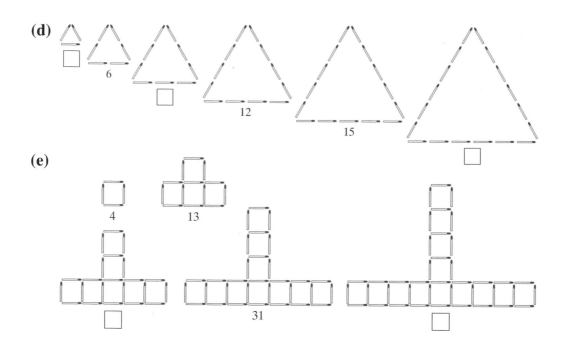

(e)

5.2 Number machines

You can use number machines to make number patterns.

A number machine performs an operation on a number:

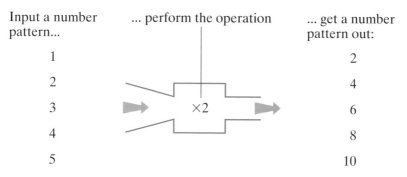

Input a number pattern...	... perform the operation	... get a number pattern out:
1		2
2	×2	4
3		6
4		8
5		10

You can show this in a table:

input	output
1	2
2	4
3	6
4	8
5	10

Example 1

Complete this table for a '×3' number machine:

×3

input	output
1	
2	
3	
4	
5	

The output numbers are the input numbers after they have gone through the number machine.

×3

input	output
1	3
2	6
3	9
4	12
5	15

Example 2

This two-step number machine performs the operation ×2 + 3:

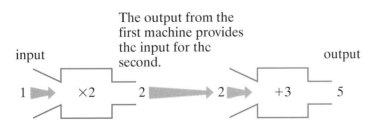

input   The output from the first machine provides the input for the second.   output

1 ▶ ×2 2 ▶ 2 ▶ +3 5

You can also use a table for two-step number machines:

$1 \times 2 = 2 \quad 2 + 3 = 5$

$2 \times 2 = 4 \quad 4 + 3 = 7$

and so on...

×2 +3

input	output
1	5
2	7
3	9
4	11
5	13

Exercise 5B

1 For each question:
   - complete the table to show the output numbers
   - describe the output pattern.

   The first one has been done for you.

(a)

+8	
1	9
2	10
3	11
4	12
5	13

operation

output numbers

input numbers

(b)

−6	
10	
11	
12	
13	
14	

(c)

×4	
3	
4	
5	
6	
7	

(d)

+12	
15	
17	
19	
21	
23	

(e)

×7	
3	
4	
5	
6	
7	

(f)

÷6	
36	
42	
48	
54	
60	

(g)

÷9	
27	
36	
45	
54	
63	

(h)

×6	
8	
9	
10	
11	
12	

(i)

−12	
18	
19	
20	
21	
22	

(j)

×5 → −2	
1	
2	
3	
4	
5	

(k)

+5 → ×4	
1	
2	
3	
4	
5	

(l)

−3 → ×2	
1	
2	
3	
4	
5	

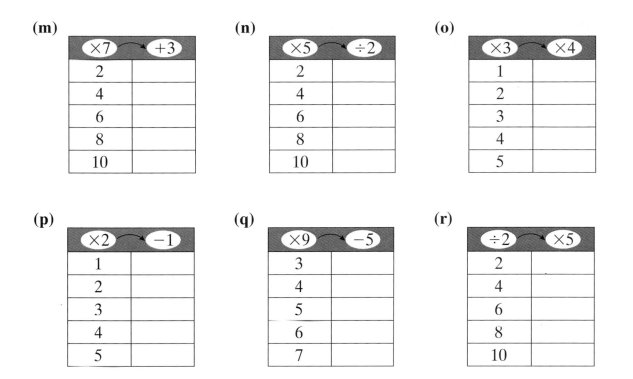

(m)

×7 → +3	
2	
4	
6	
8	
10	

(n)

×5 → ÷2	
2	
4	
6	
8	
10	

(o)

×3 → ×4	
1	
2	
3	
4	
5	

(p)

×2 → −1	
1	
2	
3	
4	
5	

(q)

×9 → −5	
3	
4	
5	
6	
7	

(r)

÷2 → ×5	
2	
4	
6	
8	
10	

5.3 Inverse operations

This number machine multiplies the input number by 2:

× **2** is called the **operation**.

To undo the operation × 2 you divide by 2:

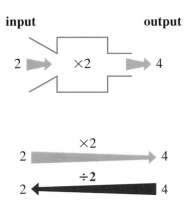

A surgeon operates on a patient.

A number machine operates on the input number.

÷2 is the **inverse** operation of ×2

The inverse 'undoes' the operation.

Example 3

Find the missing input numbers by using the correct inverse operation.

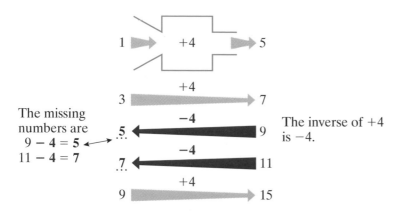

The missing numbers are
$9 - 4 = 5$
$11 - 4 = 7$

The inverse of $+4$ is -4.

Use this table to help you find the inverse operation:

Operation	Inverse
+	−
−	+
×	÷
÷	×

Exercise 5C

1   Use inverses to complete each table.

(a)

+5	
14	19
...	22
20	25
...	28

(b)

÷3	
36	12
...	13
42	14
...	15

(c)

÷2	
...	4
12	6
16	8
...	10

(d)

×5	
...	20
6	30
...	40
10	50

(e)

+10	
22	32
...	33
...	34
25	35

(f)

−4	
52	48
...	58
...	68
82	78

(g)

+50	
50	100
100	150
...	200
...	250

(h)

×10	
...	40
6	60
...	80
10	100

(i)

$+\frac{1}{2}$	
...	$1\frac{1}{2}$
$1\frac{1}{2}$	2
2	$2\frac{1}{2}$
...	3

(j)

÷0.5	
12	24
...	28
...	32
18	36

5.4 Number sequences

Each number in a sequence is called a **term**:

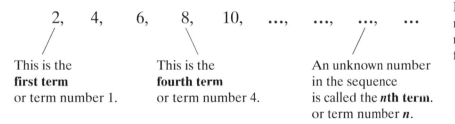

2,   4,   6,   8,   10,   ...,   ...,   ...,   ...

This is the
first term
or term number 1.

This is the
fourth term
or term number 4.

An unknown number
in the sequence
is called the **nth term**.
or term number **n**.

For this work you
need to know about
multiples and
factors see p. 49.

When exploring number sequences you can find:

■   a rule to find the next term.
■   a rule to find the *n*th term.

Finding the next term

To find the next term in this sequence, add 2:

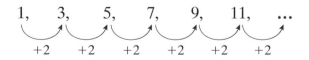

1,   3,   5,   7,   9,   11,   ...

+2   +2   +2   +2   +2   +2

The difference
between each term
and the next is +2.

The next term is **13** and the rule is **+2**.

Example 4

3, 6, 12, 24 ...

The next term is **48** and the rule is **×2**.

This time you have to × 2 to get the next term.

Exercise 5D

1 For each question, write down the next term and the rule you used.

(a) 1, 4, 7, 10, ...   (b) 8, 16, 24, ...
(c) 20, 18, 16, ...   (d) 60, 50, 40, ...
(e) 9, 18, 27, ...   (f) 5, 10, 20, ...
(g) 32, 16, 8, ...   (h) 10 000, 1000, 100, ...

Finding the *n*th term

You can use algebra to write a rule to find any number in a sequence. This rule is called the **nth term rule** or the **general rule**.

Example 5

Find the general rule for this sequence:

6, 12, 18, 24, 30, ...

Write the sequence and the term numbers in a table:

Term number	Sequence
1 — ×6 →	6
2 — ×6 →	12
3 — ×6 →	18
4 — ×6 →	24
5 — ×6 →	30
⋮	⋮
n — ×6 →	$6n$

The general rule for this sequence is: the **nth term** is **6*n***

Exercise 5E

1 Find the general rule for each of these sequences:

(a)

Term number	Sequence
1 —— +7 —→ 8	
2 —— +7 —→ 9	
3 —— +7 —→ 10	
4 —— +7 —→ 11	
5 —— +7 —→ 12	
⋮	
n —— +7 —→	

(b)

Term number	Sequence
1 —— ×5 —→ 5	
2 —— ×5 —→ 10	
3 —— ×5 —→ 15	
4 —— ×5 —→ 20	
5 —— ×5 —→ 25	
⋮	⋮
n —— ×5 —→	

(c)

Term number	Sequence
1 —→ 9	
2 —→ 18	
3 —→ 27	
4 —→ 36	
5 —→ 45	

(d)

Term number	Sequence
1 —→ 19	
2 —→ 20	
3 —→ 21	
4 —→ 22	
5 —→ 23	

(e)

Term number	Sequence
1 —→ −1	
2 —→ 0	
3 —→ 1	
4 —→ 2	
5 —→ 3	

(f)

Term number	Sequence
1	2
2	4
3	6
4	8
5	10

(g)

Term number	Sequence
1	100
2	200
3	300
4	400
5	500

(h)

Term number	Sequence
1	1
2	4
3	9
4	16
5	25

(i)

Term number	Sequence
1	3
2	5
3	7
4	9
5	11

(j)

Term number	Sequence
1	5
2	8
3	11
4	14
5	17

2 For these sequences put the information into a table and write the general rule:

(a) 6, 7, 8, 9, 10, . . . **(b)** 3, 6, 9, 12, 15, . . .
(c) 7, 14, 21, 28, 35, . . . **(d)** 18, 19, 20, 21, . . .
(e) 50, 100, 150, 200, . . . **(f)** 0, 1, 2, 3, 4, . . .
(g) −3, −2, −1, 0, 1, 2, . . . **(h)** 11, 22, 33, 44, . . .
(i) 13, 14, 15, 16, . . . **(j)** $\frac{1}{2}$, 1, $1\frac{1}{2}$, 2, $2\frac{1}{2}$, . . .

Finding terms

To calculate a term you need to know the general rule.

Example 6

Find the 20th and 49th terms if the general rule is:
nth term is $8n$

$8n = 8 \times n$

If nth term is $8n$
20th term is 8×20
$= 160$

If nth term is $8n$
49th term is 8×49
$= 392$

Exercise 5F

1. (a) Find the 10th term if the nth term is $4n$
   (b) Find the 7th term if the nth term is $n + 2$
   (c) Find the 100th term if the nth term is $5n$
   (d) Find the 20th term if the nth term is $n - 10$
   (e) Find the 8th term if the nth term is $n + 5$
   (f) Find the 15th term if the nth term is $n \div 3$
   (g) Find the 12th term if the nth term is $2n$
   (h) Find the 30th term if the nth term is $n + 6$
   (i) Find the 40th term if the nth term is $n \div 2$
   (j) Find the 50th term if the nth term is $n - 25$

Summary of key points

1. When exploring number sequences you can find:
   - a rule to find the **next term**.
   - a rule to find the **nth term**.

6 Fractions

You can find fractions all around:

This stained glass window is in 4 equal parts.
Each part is one **quarter** of the window.

This cake is cut into 8 equal slices.
Each part is one **eighth** of the cake.

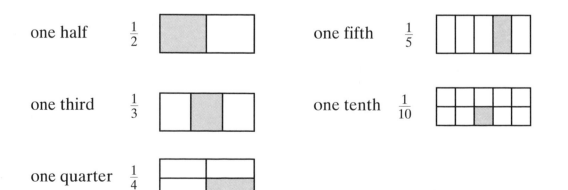

A football pitch is divided into two **halves**.

You should recognise these common fractions:

one half $\frac{1}{2}$

one third $\frac{1}{3}$

one quarter $\frac{1}{4}$

one fifth $\frac{1}{5}$

one tenth $\frac{1}{10}$

6.1 Finding fractions of quantities

Sometimes you will need to find a fraction of a quantity.
For example, to find $\frac{5}{6}$ of 18, first find $\frac{1}{6}$ of 18:

To find $\frac{1}{6}$ divide by the denominator 6:

Remember:
this number is the
numerator

$$\frac{3}{4}$$

this number is the
denominator

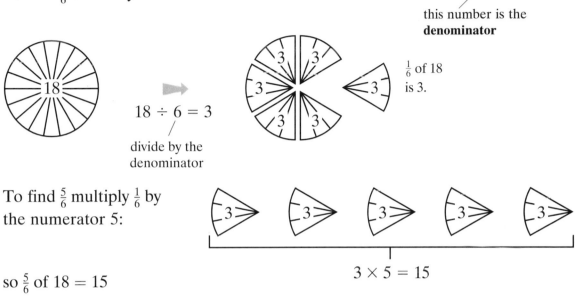

$18 \div 6 = 3$

divide by the
denominator

$\frac{1}{6}$ of 18
is 3.

To find $\frac{5}{6}$ multiply $\frac{1}{6}$ by
the numerator 5:

$3 \times 5 = 15$

so $\frac{5}{6}$ of 18 = 15

Example 1

Find $\frac{3}{4}$ of 28.

$\frac{1}{4}$ of 28 is $28 \div 4 = 7$

divide by the
denominator

$7 \times 3 = 21$

multiply by numerator

so $\frac{3}{4}$ of 28 = 21

You can do this
instead:

$$\frac{3}{4} \text{ of } 28$$

$3 \times 28 = 84$
$84 \div 4 = 21$

to get the same
answer.

Example 2

Kiesha got $\frac{5}{8}$ of her test correct.

There were 152 questions in total.
How many did she get right?

$\frac{1}{8}$ of 152 is $152 \div 8 = 19$

so $\frac{5}{8}$ of 152 is $5 \times 19 = 95$

Keisha got 95 questions right.

Using a calculator
you could do this
instead:

$5 \times 152 = 760$
$760 \div 8 = 95$

Exercise 6A

1 (a) Find one half of sixty.
   (b) Find one fifth of 55 sweets.
   (c) Find two eighths of 56 grams.

2 Find:
   (a) $\frac{2}{3}$ of 24   (b) $\frac{5}{6}$ of 18   (c) $\frac{3}{10}$ of 90   (d) $\frac{4}{11}$ of 55 m   (e) $\frac{7}{8}$ of 32 minutes

3 Lil sat a driving theory test.
   To pass she must get $\frac{6}{7}$ of the questions correct.
   How many questions must she get correct to pass?

Driving
theory
test:
35 questions

4 (a) Susan ate one third of a bag of 39 sweets.
        How many did she eat?
        How many were left in the bag?
   (b) Andrew earns £120 each week. He pays one fifth of
        this in tax. How much does he have left?
   (c) Christine was watching television. She saw $\frac{2}{3}$ of the
        45 minute programme before the telephone rang.
        How much of the programme did she miss?
   (d) Kevin watched $\frac{7}{10}$ of the 90 minute football match.
        Keith watched $\frac{5}{9}$ of the same match.
        Who saw more of the game?

5 David, Maureen and Steven all run a race of 400 m.
   David runs $\frac{5}{8}$ of the distance and stops as he is tired.
   Maureen runs $\frac{3}{4}$ of the distance before she gets tired.
   Steven runs $\frac{19}{20}$ of the distance and then stops as he
   realises he has won.
   How many metres has each person run?

6.2 Equivalent fractions

Ayana, Louise and Adam are eating cake:

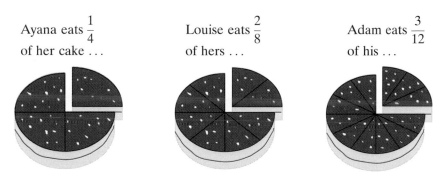

Ayana eats $\frac{1}{4}$ of her cake . . .

Louise eats $\frac{2}{8}$ of hers . . .

Adam eats $\frac{3}{12}$ of his . . .

The fractions $\frac{1}{4}$, $\frac{2}{8}$ and $\frac{3}{12}$ all represent the same amount of cake.

- **Fractions that have the same value are called equivalent fractions.**

  For example, $\frac{1}{4} = \frac{2}{8} = \frac{3}{12}$

Equivalent fractions can be found by multiplying or dividing the numerator and denominator by the same number. For example:

$$\frac{1}{3} \quad \boxed{\begin{array}{l}\text{1 multiplied by 2 is 2}\\\text{3 multiplied by 2 is 6}\end{array}} \quad \frac{2}{6} \quad \boxed{\begin{array}{l}\text{2 multiplied by 3 is 6}\\\text{6 multiplied by 3 is 18}\end{array}} \quad \frac{6}{18}$$

or $\quad \dfrac{1}{3} \quad \boxed{\begin{array}{l}\text{1 multiplied by 7 is 7}\\\text{3 multiplied by 7 is 21}\end{array}} \quad \dfrac{7}{21}$

so $\quad \frac{1}{3} \;=\; \frac{2}{6} \;=\; \frac{6}{18} \;=\; \frac{7}{21} \quad$ are equivalent fractions

Also:

$$\frac{30}{40} \quad \boxed{\begin{array}{l}\text{30 divided by 2 is 15}\\\text{40 divided by 2 is 20}\end{array}} \quad \frac{15}{20} \quad \boxed{\begin{array}{l}\text{15 divided by 5 is 3}\\\text{20 divided by 5 is 4}\end{array}} \quad \frac{3}{4}$$

Notice that $\frac{3}{4}$ is the **simplest form** of the fraction $\frac{30}{40}$.

There is no equivalent fraction with smaller numbers on the top and bottom.

Example 3

Complete this set of equivalent fractions.

(a) $\frac{1}{2} = \frac{}{4} = \frac{}{10}$

(b) $\frac{24}{32} = \frac{}{16} = \frac{}{4}$

(a) Multiply the numerator and denominator by 2:

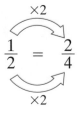

Multiply the numerator and denominator by 5:

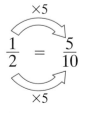

So the set of equivalent fractions is:

$$\frac{1}{2} = \frac{2}{4} = \frac{5}{10}$$

(b) Divide the numerator and denominator by 2 ...

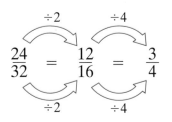

Dividing top and bottom by the same number is called **cancelling**.

... and then divide again by 4

Exercise 6B

1   Copy these sets of fractions. Fill in the missing numbers to make the fractions equivalent.

(a) $\frac{1}{4} = \frac{?}{8} = \frac{6}{?} = \frac{3}{?}$

(b) $\frac{2}{5} = \frac{4}{?} = \frac{?}{15} = \frac{10}{?}$

(c) $\frac{3}{10} = \frac{6}{?} = \frac{9}{?} = \frac{?}{100}$

2 Nick and Harry each have the same amount of pocket money. Harry spends two tenths of his money. Nick spends four twentieths of his. Does Nick spend more than Harry? Explain your answer.

3 Which of these fractions are the same?

$$\frac{1}{4} \qquad \frac{6}{10} \qquad \frac{4}{9} \qquad \frac{7}{12} \qquad \frac{35}{50}$$

$$\frac{5}{6} \qquad \frac{7}{10} \qquad \frac{2}{3} \qquad \frac{3}{5} \qquad \frac{16}{36} \qquad \frac{15}{18}$$

4 Find all the sets of equivalent fractions.

$$\frac{6}{21} \qquad \frac{18}{24} \qquad \frac{1}{5} \qquad \frac{25}{40} \qquad \frac{14}{49} \qquad \frac{10}{16}$$

$$\frac{3}{15} \qquad \frac{10}{50} \qquad \frac{5}{8} \qquad \frac{12}{16} \qquad \frac{2}{7} \qquad \frac{3}{4}$$

6.3 Putting fractions in order of size

Which is larger $\frac{1}{3}$ or $\frac{2}{5}$?

Change the fractions so that they have the same denominator:

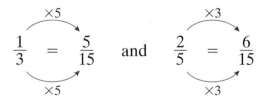

$$\frac{1}{3} = \frac{5}{15} \quad \text{and} \quad \frac{2}{5} = \frac{6}{15}$$

15 is the smallest number that is a multiple of 3 and 5. It is called the **lowest common multiple** of 3 and 5.

$\frac{6}{15}$ is larger than $\frac{5}{15}$

so $\frac{2}{5}$ must be larger than $\frac{1}{3}$.

Exercise 6C

1. Find the fraction between $\frac{6}{12}$ and $\frac{10}{12}$ which is equivalent to two thirds.

2. Change the following fractions to fractions with the same denominator. Then put them in order of size:

   $\frac{2}{3}, \frac{5}{12}, \frac{5}{6}, \frac{3}{4}$

3. John needs to fill $\frac{3}{10}$ of a beaker with water for a science experiment. The beaker was marked in twentieths. He filled it up to the thirteenth mark $\left(\frac{13}{20}\right)$.

   Explain what he did wrong.

4. Which is bigger: $\frac{3}{5}, \frac{3}{6}$ or $\frac{3}{4}$?

5. What would you rather have $\frac{3}{5}$ or $\frac{7}{10}$ of a bar of chocolate?

6. Carmella and Alex both walk to school.
   When Alex has walked $\frac{11}{15}$ of the distance, Carmella has walked $\frac{4}{5}$ of the distance.

   Who has walked the furthest distance at this point?

6.4 Types of fractions

How many pizzas are there?

$1\frac{1}{2}$ or $\frac{3}{2}$?

This means
3 halves

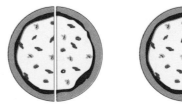

Both answers are correct.
Sometimes you will need to use **mixed numbers** and **improper fractions**.

- **A mixed number is a mixture of a whole number and a fraction.**

  $1\frac{1}{2}$, $2\frac{1}{3}$, $10\frac{4}{7}$, $9\frac{2}{5}$, are all mixed numbers.

- **An improper fraction has a numerator that is larger than the denominator.**

  $\frac{3}{2}$, $\frac{9}{5}$, $\frac{4}{3}$, $\frac{17}{4}$, are all improper fractions.

Improper fractions are also called 'top-heavy' fractions.

You can change a mixed number into an improper fraction like this:

$$1\frac{3}{5} = \frac{5}{5} + \frac{3}{5} = \frac{8}{5}$$

So $1\frac{3}{5}$ is the same as $\frac{8}{5}$.

You can change an improper fraction into a mixed number like this:

$$\frac{13}{6} = \frac{6}{6} + \frac{6}{6} + \frac{1}{6} = 2\frac{1}{6}$$

So $\frac{13}{6}$ is equivalent to $2\frac{1}{6}$.

Hint:
Any fraction with the numerator and denominator the same is equal to 1.

$1 = \frac{1}{1} = \frac{2}{2} = \frac{3}{3} = \frac{4}{4}\ldots$

Example 4

Change $\frac{9}{8}$ to a mixed number.

$$\frac{9}{8} = \frac{8}{8} + \frac{1}{8} = 1 + \frac{1}{8} = 1\frac{1}{8}$$

$9 \div 8 = 1$
with a remainder
of 1 part
$1\frac{1}{8}$

Exercise 6D

1 How many fifths are there in two?

2 How many sixths are there in four?

3 How many tenths are there in three?

4 How many thirds are there in six?

5 How many halves are there in ten?

Hint:
$1 = \frac{5}{5}$ so $2 = \frac{10}{5}$

6 Change these improper fractions to mixed numbers.

(a) $\frac{5}{2}$ (b) seven quarters   (c) $\frac{11}{5}$ (d) $\frac{7}{3}$

(e) eleven ninths   (f) $\frac{19}{10}$ (g) $\frac{13}{4}$ (h) thirteen eighths

7 Change these mixed numbers to improper fractions.

(a) $1\frac{3}{4}$ (b) one and a half

(c) one and two thirds   (d) $5\frac{1}{4}$

(e) $3\frac{2}{5}$ (f) $3\frac{5}{8}$

8 Find the matching pairs of fractions in the diagram.

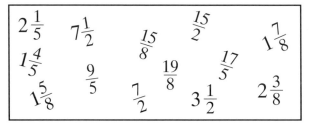

$2\frac{1}{5}$ $7\frac{1}{2}$ $\frac{15}{8}$ $\frac{15}{2}$ $1\frac{7}{8}$

$1\frac{4}{5}$ $\frac{9}{5}$ $\frac{19}{8}$ $\frac{17}{5}$

$1\frac{5}{8}$ $\frac{7}{2}$ $3\frac{1}{2}$ $2\frac{3}{8}$

6.5 Adding and subtracting fractions

It is easy to add or subtract fractions if they belong to the same fraction family.

$1 + 1 = 2$

$$\frac{1}{3} \quad + \quad \frac{1}{3} \quad = \quad \frac{2}{3}$$

$3 - 1 = 2$

$$\frac{3}{5} \quad - \quad \frac{1}{5} \quad = \quad \frac{2}{5}$$

Remember:
The denominator of a fraction tells you the fraction family:

$$\frac{5}{7}$$

The fraction family is sevenths.

The answer is in the same fraction family, thirds.

_____ Keep the same denominator

■ **To add or subtract fractions with the same denominator add or subtract the numerators and write the result over the same denominator.**

Example 5

Work out:

(a) $\frac{1}{10} + \frac{2}{10}$ **(b)** $\frac{7}{8} - \frac{3}{8}$

(a) The fraction family is the same so just add:

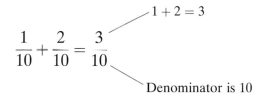

$1 + 2 = 3$

$$\frac{1}{10} + \frac{2}{10} = \frac{3}{10}$$

Denominator is 10

(b) Both denominators are the same so just subtract:

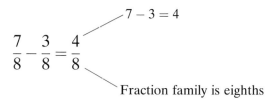

$7 - 3 = 4$

$$\frac{7}{8} - \frac{3}{8} = \frac{4}{8}$$

Fraction family is eighths

Adding and subtracting fractions with different denominators

Donna gets $\frac{1}{3}$ of her homework done at school.

She does $\frac{1}{4}$ of it before dinner.

How much of her homework has she done?

To add the fractions find equivalent fractions with the same denominators:

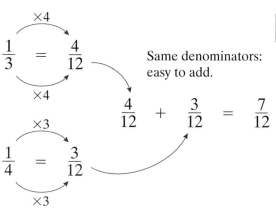

$\times 4$

$$\frac{1}{3} = \frac{4}{12}$$

$\times 4$

Same denominators: easy to add.

$$\frac{4}{12} + \frac{3}{12} = \frac{7}{12}$$

$\times 3$

$$\frac{1}{4} = \frac{3}{12}$$

$\times 3$

so $\frac{1}{3} + \frac{1}{4} = \frac{4}{12} + \frac{3}{12} = \frac{7}{12}$

Example 6

Work out $\frac{1}{6} + \frac{3}{4}$

Find equivalent fractions with the same denominator:

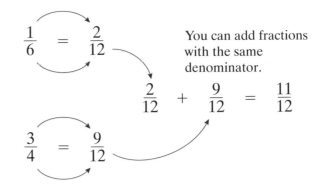

■ **To add (or subtract) fractions with different denominators find equivalent fractions with the same denominators.**

Exercise 6E

1   Add the following fractions:

  (a) $\frac{1}{9} + \frac{2}{9}$ **(b)** $\frac{3}{7} + \frac{1}{7}$ **(c)** $\frac{2}{11} + \frac{5}{11}$ **(d)** $\frac{1}{8} + \frac{2}{8}$

  (e) Find an equivalent fraction for each of your answers.

2   Subtract the following fractions:

  (a) $\frac{4}{10} - \frac{1}{10}$ **(b)** $\frac{3}{13} - \frac{2}{13}$ **(c)** $\frac{11}{12} - \frac{2}{12}$

  (d) Find an equivalent fraction for each of your answers.

3   Erin had $\frac{3}{8}$m of a roll of paper, she gave $\frac{1}{8}$m to Marie. How much did she have left?

4   James cycles $\frac{4}{8}$ of the way to school. He gets a flat tyre and has to walk for $\frac{3}{8}$ of the journey to a garage to be able to fix his bike. How far had he still to go to school?

5   Add the following fractions:

  (a) $\frac{2}{5} + \frac{1}{8}$ **(b)** $\frac{7}{10} + \frac{1}{20}$ **(c)** $\frac{3}{4} + \frac{1}{9}$

  (d) $\frac{4}{15} + \frac{1}{30}$ **(e)** $\frac{5}{9} + \frac{2}{3}$ **(f)** $\frac{7}{12} + \frac{5}{8}$

6 Morgan is listening to the radio in his car. He listens to jazz for half the journey and the news for a third of his journey. He then turns the radio off.
For what fraction of the journey does he listen to the radio?

7 Subtract the following fractions:

(a) $\frac{9}{10} - \frac{2}{5}$ (b) $\frac{3}{4} - \frac{7}{20}$ (c) $\frac{7}{8} - \frac{5}{6}$

(d) $\frac{9}{10} - \frac{4}{15}$ (e) $\frac{3}{4} - \frac{3}{20}$ (f) $\frac{8}{12} - \frac{1}{4}$

8 Gina and Paul went on holiday to France. They spent $\frac{3}{10}$ of the day playing sport. $\frac{1}{5}$ was spent on swimming, how much of their time was left for other sports?

Summary of key points

1 Fractions that have the same value are called equivalent fractions.

2 A mixed number is a mixture of a whole number and a fraction.

$1\frac{1}{2}$, $2\frac{1}{3}$, $10\frac{4}{7}$, $9\frac{2}{5}$, are all mixed numbers.

3 An improper fraction has a numerator that is larger than the denominator.

$\frac{3}{2}$, $\frac{9}{5}$, $\frac{4}{3}$, $\frac{17}{4}$, are all improper fractions.

4 To add or subtract fractions with the same denominator add or subtract the numerators and write the result over the same denominator.

5 To add (or subtract) fractions with different denominators find equivalent fractions with the same denominators.

7 Probability

What are your chances of ...

... tossing a head?

"fifty-fifty"

.. being struck by lightning?

"1 in 200 000"

... winning the jackpot?

"1 in 14 million"

... proving Fermat's last theorem?

Andrew Wiles did in 1994

Probability uses numbers to represent the chance or likelihood that something will happen.

7.1 Certain, impossible or possible?

You can show how likely it is that something will happen on a **likelihood scale**:

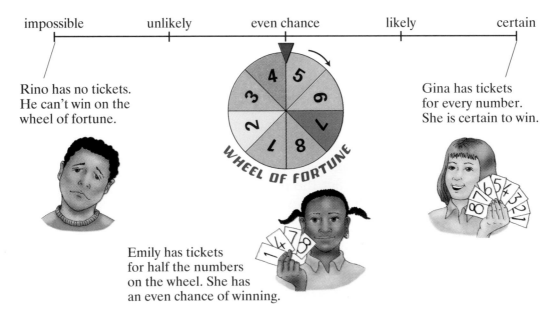

impossible   unlikely   even chance   likely   certain

Rino has no tickets. He can't win on the wheel of fortune.

Gina has tickets for every number. She is certain to win.

Emily has tickets for half the numbers on the wheel. She has an even chance of winning.

WHEEL OF FORTUNE

Example 1

Draw a likelihood scale. On it mark the likelihood that:
(a) The next person to book a holiday will be male.
(b) It will snow in Australia on Christmas day this year.
(c) A woman will captain the women's rugby team.
(d) A train will be late tomorrow.
(e) You can learn Japanese in one day.

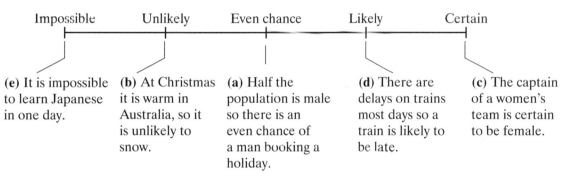

Impossible	Unlikely	Even chance	Likely	Certain

(e) It is impossible to learn Japanese in one day.

(b) At Christmas it is warm in Australia, so it is unlikely to snow.

(a) Half the population is male so there is an even chance of a man booking a holiday.

(d) There are delays on trains most days so a train is likely to be late.

(c) The captain of a women's team is certain to be female.

Example 2

Copy and complete the sentences below using these words:

chance   likely   unlikely   certain   impossible   even chance

(a) It is _____ that I will win the national lottery jackpot.
(b) Bijit is good at maths; he is _____ to get all his homework correct.
(c) The coin had an _____ of landing heads up.

(a) It is **unlikely** that I will win the national lottery jackpot.
(b) Bijit is good at maths; he is **certain** to get all his homework correct.
(c) The coin had an **even chance** of landing heads up.

Exercise 7A

1   Draw a likelihood scale. On it mark the likelihood that:
(a) You will get an eight when you roll a normal dice.
(b) The leaning tower of Pisa will fall over tomorrow.
(c) Tuesday will be the day after Monday next week.
(d) You will watch a film this month.
(e) Every student in your class is over six years old.
(f) Every student in your class will study mathematics at university.
(g) The next person you talk to will speak Urdu.

So far the leaning tower of Pisa has been standing for over 600 years.

2   Copy the sentences below and use the blue words to fill in the gaps:

Chance   **Likely**   **Unlikely**

Certain   **Impossible**   **Even chance**

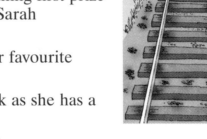

(a) It is _____ for a dog to run at 80 km/h.

(b) I am _____ to phone a friend this evening.

(c) You have an _____ of choosing black when you play chess.

(d) It is _____ that parallel lines will never cross.

(e) 'I have a very good _____ of winning first prize in the Chemistry competition' said Sarah Scientificus.

(f) Yvonne was _____ to choose her favourite colour when buying a new dress.

(g) Shereen is _____ to walk to work as she has a new car.

3   Use the blue words in question **2** to make up 6 sentences of your own.

7.2 Using numbers to represent probabilities

You can use numbers to show how likely it is that something will happen.

Look at this **probability scale**:

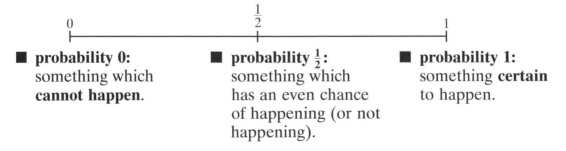

- **probability 0:** something which **cannot happen**.

- **probability $\frac{1}{2}$:** something which has an even chance of happening (or not happening).

- **probability 1:** something **certain** to happen.

- **Probability uses numbers to represent the chance that something will happen.**

- **All probabilities have a value from 0 to 1.**

You can write probabilities as fractions, decimals or percentages.

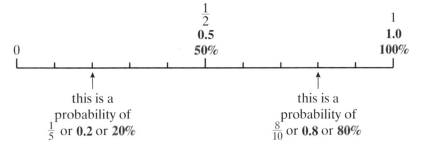

There is more about decimals and percentages on p 128

Example 3

Mark these on a probability scale.
Give a reason for your answer.

(a) A family owns a caravan.

(b) You will blink in the next minute.

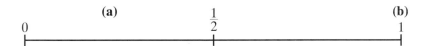

(a) Is unlikely. In any road only a few families will own a caravan.

(b) Is certain. A person blinks every few seconds.

Example 4

What is the probability of:

(a) landing on heads when you toss a coin?

(b) the sun rising tomorrow?

Write your answer as a fraction, decimal and percentage.

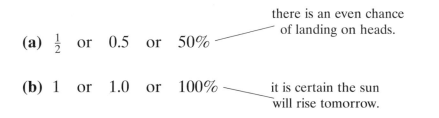

(a) $\frac{1}{2}$ or 0.5 or 50% — there is an even chance of landing on heads.

(b) 1 or 1.0 or 100% — it is certain the sun will rise tomorrow.

Exercise 7B

1 Draw a probability scale and mark each of these on it.
Give a reason for each answer.

(a) You will get a flat tyre next time you ride a bicycle.
(b) The black cat will be the first to catch the mouse

(c) Your hair will grow 4 inches overnight.
(d) On Christmas Day you will eat brussels sprouts.
(e) You will wear school uniform on Sunday.
(f) Ice cream sales rise in the summer.
(g) The next baby to be born will be a boy or a girl.
(h) You will visit Mars next week.
(i) You will eat fish and chips every night this week.
(j) It will take the Earth 24 hours to complete one full
turn.

2 The letters A to E are marked on this probability scale.
Write down something to match each letter.

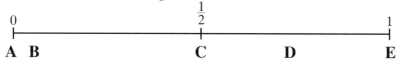

Hint: C must be something with an even chance of happening.

3 Rachel has a bag of 50 fruit chews. 10 of the chews have
green wrappers. What is the probability that Rachel will
randomly pick a chew with a green wrapper?
Write your answer as:

(a) a fraction   **(b)** a decimal   **(c)** a percentage

4 A box has 20 cubes in it. Eight of the cubes are red.
Cheryl takes a cube out of the box without looking.
Which of these values show the probability that Cheryl
takes out a red cube?

$\frac{8}{10}$ 0.4   50%

0.8 $\frac{8}{20}$ 0.40%

40%   0.75 $\frac{2}{5}$

Hint:
There are 4 correct
answers.

5 A bag has 40 beads in it. 12 of the beads are blue. Adrian takes a bead out of the bag without looking. What is the probability that the bead Adrian takes is blue?
Write your answer as:
(a) a fraction (b) a decimal (c) a percentage

7.3 Events and outcomes

You need to know the difference between an **event** and an **outcome**:

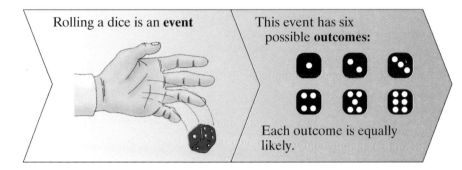

Rolling a dice is an **event**

This event has six possible **outcomes:**

Each outcome is equally likely.

Example 5

A computer is programmed to play one of eight notes at random.

List all of the possible outcomes.

The possible outcomes are:

low C, D, E, F, G, A, B, high C

All of the outcomes are equally likely.

At random means that each note has an equal chance of being played.

Example 6

This spinner is used to choose a colour. List all the equally likely outcomes.

There are five equally likely outcomes:

red, blue, green, yellow and orange.

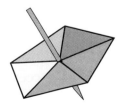

Exercise 7C

1   List all the outcomes for the following events.

   (a) Choosing a coin from this purse.

   (b) Tossing a coin.

   (c) Choosing a cake from this packet.

   (d) Choosing a card from the picture cards only.

   (e) Spinning this spinner:

   (f) Throwing a coin and a dice.

   (g) Choosing a shape from the regular polygons with less than ten sides.

   (h) Choosing 2 beads from this bag: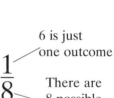

7.4 Calculating probabilities

Sometimes you can **calculate** the probability that something will happen.

There are 8 possible outcomes when you spin this spinner:

Landing on 6 is just 1 of the 8 outcomes.

The probability of landing on 6 is $\frac{1}{8}$:

$$\frac{1}{8}$$

6 is just one outcome

There are 8 possible outcomes

You can write the probability like this:

probability (land on 6) $= \frac{1}{8}$

or   P (land on 6) $= \frac{1}{8}$

■ **The probability that something will happen is:**

$$\textbf{P(event)} = \frac{\textbf{number of successful outcomes}}{\textbf{total number of possible outcomes}}$$

This is sometimes called the **theoretical probability** because you can calculate it without doing an experiment.

Example 7

Calculate the probability of picking the letter R from the letters in the name CHRISTABEL.

There are 10 possible outcomes when picking a letter at random. There is only one letter R, so:

probability (choosing R) $= \frac{1}{10}$ or $P(R) = \frac{1}{10}$

Example 8

This bag contains 4 red peppers, 3 green peppers and 2 yellow peppers. What is the probability that a pepper picked at random from the bag will be green.

There are 9 peppers. 3 are green so:

$P(green) = \frac{3}{9} = \frac{1}{3}$

Remember:

$\frac{1}{3}$ is $\frac{3}{9}$

in its **simplest form**.

Exercise 7D

1   An eight sided die is rolled once.
   (a) What is the probability of rolling a 3?
   (b) What is the probability of rolling a 9?
   (c) What is the probability of rolling an
        even number?

2 The 30 days of June are written as
numbers on cards and placed in a bag.
A card is picked from the bag.

(a) What is the probability of choosing day 13?

(b) The second of June is a Monday.
What is the probability of choosing a Monday?

(c) Jan can go to the dentist on any day except
Saturday and Sunday. What is the probability that
she chooses a day on which she can go?

(d) Jerry can go to a club on even days only. What is
the probability that he chooses a day on which he
can go clubbing?

3 Design 6 robots, so that

- The probability of picking a green robot is $\frac{2}{6}$
- The probability of picking a black robot is 0
- The probability of picking a robot with 1 central eye is $\frac{1}{6}$
- The probability of a robot having large ears is $\frac{4}{6}$
- The probability of a robot having 4 arms is $\frac{1}{3}$

4 A PE teacher picks one of these girls at random to be
team captain. What is the probability that the chosen
girl will:

(a) have long hair   (b) have a ponytail
(c) wear glasses   (d) be wearing shorts
(e) have long trousers on

5 A card is chosen from a shuffled pack of 52 playing
cards. What is the probability of choosing:

(a) a red king   (b) an ace
(c) a spade   (d) a red card
(e) nine of diamonds   (f) a picture card

6   A variety pack of biscuits contains 3 hobnobs, 2 chocolate digestives, 1 custard cream, 4 jammy dodgers, 8 rich tea biscuits and 5 chocolate fingers. What is the probability of choosing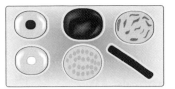

   (a) jammy dodger?   **(b)** a hobnob?

   (c) a custard cream?   **(d)** a biscuit that contains chocolate?

   (e) a biscuit that contains no chocolate?

   (f) a biscuit other than a custard cream?

7.5 Probabilities that add to 1

When you roll a dice …

the probability of **getting a 3** is:

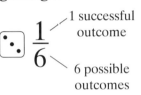

$\dfrac{1}{6}$ 1 successful outcome / 6 possible outcomes

… the probability of **not getting** a 3 is:

$\dfrac{5}{6}$ 5 unsuccessful outcomes / 6 possible outcomes

Notice that:

$$P(\text{roll a } 3) + P(\text{not roll a } 3) = \tfrac{1}{6} + \tfrac{5}{6} = \tfrac{6}{6} = 1$$

■   **The probabilities of all possible outcomes of an event add up to 1.**

Example 9

There are five balls in this bag. Two balls are blue. If you pick one ball at random what is the probability of:

(a) picking a blue ball?   **(b)** not picking a blue ball?

(a) Two balls are blue so:

$$P(\text{pick a blue ball}) = \tfrac{2}{5}$$

(b) As $P(\text{pick a blue ball}) + P(\text{not pick a blue ball}) = 1$

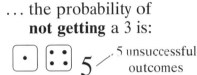

$$\tfrac{2}{5} \qquad + \qquad ? \qquad = 1$$

at random means the chance of picking each ball is the same – you can't see into the bag!

? must be $\tfrac{3}{5}$ so:

$$P(\text{not pick a blue ball}) = \tfrac{3}{5}$$

■ **If the probability of an event happening is P, then
the probability of it not happening is 1 − P.**

Example 10

The probability of winning a prize in the school raffle is $\frac{1}{20}$.
What is the probability of not winning a prize?

$$P\,(\text{not winning}) = 1 - P\,(\text{winning})$$
$$= 1 - \tfrac{1}{20}$$
$$= \tfrac{19}{20}$$

Exercise 7E

1   Ann, Brenda and Carly are entered
    for a race as the only three runners.
    The probability of Ann winning is $\frac{2}{7}$,
    the probability of Brenda winning is $\frac{3}{7}$.
    What is the probability of
    (a) Carly winning?
    (b) Brenda not winning?
    (c) Ann not winning?

2   The probability of rain on any day is $\frac{2}{5}$. What is the
    probability of it not raining?

3   There are 6 milk chocolates, 3 plain chocolates and
    4 white chocolates in a selection box. A chocolate is
    chosen at random, calculate the probability that:
    (a) it is a milk chocolate
    (b) it is not a milk chocolate
    (c) it is not a plain chocolate.

4   Students in a class study one of three languages.
    The probability of a pupil studying French is $\frac{4}{10}$,
    the probability of studying Spanish is $\frac{3}{10}$.
    What is the probability of a pupil studying German?

7.6 Experimenting with probability

You can estimate the probability of something happening from an experiment:

Sam rolls a die
60 times:

He gets twelve 4's
out of 60 rolls:

1	JHT IIII
2	JHT JHT
3	JHT III
4	JHT JHT II

Each roll is called
a **trial**.

The **experimental
probability** of rolling
a 4 is $\frac{12}{60}$ or $\frac{1}{5}$

12 succesful
trials ——— $\dfrac{12}{60}$ ← 60 total
trials

■ **Experimental probability** $= \dfrac{\textbf{number of successful trials}}{\textbf{total number of trials}}$

Experimental
probability is
sometimes called
the **estimated
probability**.

Example 11

Throw a coin 10 times and record the results. Repeat the
experiment. Both times calculate:
(a) the estimated probability of getting a tail
(b) the theoretical probability of getting a tail.

Experiment 1 results:

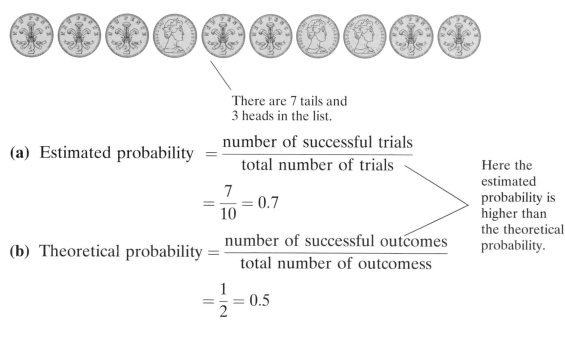

There are 7 tails and
3 heads in the list.

(a) Estimated probability $= \dfrac{\text{number of successful trials}}{\text{total number of trials}}$

$$= \frac{7}{10} = 0.7$$

(b) Theoretical probability $= \dfrac{\text{number of successful outcomes}}{\text{total number of outcomess}}$

$$= \frac{1}{2} = 0.5$$

Here the
estimated
probability is
higher than
the theoretical
probability.

Experiment 2 results:

There are 4 tails and 6 heads.

(a) Estimated probability $= \dfrac{4}{10} = 0.4$

Here the estimated probability is less than the theoretical probability.

(b) Theoretical probability $= \dfrac{\text{number of successful outcomes}}{\text{total number of outcomess}}$

$$= \dfrac{1}{2} = 0.5$$

■ **The experimental probability may vary from one experiment to the next.**
The theoretical probability is always the same.

Exercise 7F

1 Each pupil in class 7GM was given 20 Smarties.
They all counted how many blue Smarties they had and recorded the totals in a table:

Number of Smarties	10	20	50	100	200	500
Number of blue Smarties	1	3	7	15	32	90
Experimental probability						

Copy this table and fill in the experimental probabilities.

Activity

2 Copy this tally chart into your book and use it to record the result of tossing a coin 10 times:

Result	Tally	Frequency
Heads		
Tails		

Use your data to calculate the experimental and theoretical probability of landing on heads.

3 Copy the table below and use it to record the results for your whole class:

Number of trials	10	50	100	150	200
Number of heads					
Experimental probability					
Experimental probability as a decimal					

What do you notice about the experimental probability compared to the theoretical probability?

4 The number of different colours in a random selection of 1000 Jumbo jellies is shown below.

Colour	Number
Red	250
Orange	200
Black	50
Green	200
Yellow	300

(a) Work out the experimental probability for getting each colour.
   Which colour are you most likely to get?
(b) How many black jellies would you expect to get in a box of 100?

Summary of key points

1

$$0 \qquad\qquad \frac{1}{2} \qquad\qquad 1$$

probability 0: something which cannot happen.

probability $\frac{1}{2}$: something which has an even chance of happening (or not happening.

probability 1: something certain to happen.

2 Probability uses numbers to represent the chance that something will happen.

3 All probabilities have a value from 0 to 1.

4 The probability that something will happen is:

$$P(\text{event}) = \frac{\text{number of successful outcomes}}{\text{total number of possible outcomes}}$$

5 The probabilities of all possible outcomes of an event add up to 1.

6 If the probability of an event happening is P, then the probability of it not happening is $1 - P$.

7 Experimental probability $= \dfrac{\text{number of successful trials}}{\text{total number of trials}}$

8 The experimental probability may vary from one experiment to the next. The theoretical probability is always the same.

8 Decimals and percentages

Sonya swam 50 m in 36.04 seconds.
36.04 is a decimal number.

■ **In a decimal number the decimal point separates the whole number from the part that is less than one.**

This place value diagram shows what 36.04 means:

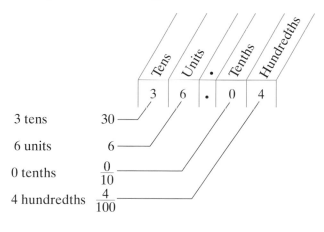

3 tens	30
6 units	6
0 tenths	$\frac{0}{10}$
4 hundredths	$\frac{4}{100}$

You say:
Thirty six point zero four.

8.1 Counting in decimals

Try counting in whole numbers.
Start at 7 and keep adding 1:

	Tens	Units
$7 + 1 = 8$		8
$8 + 1 = 9$		9
$9 + 1 = 10$	1	0
$10 + 1 = 11$	1	1
$11 + 1 = 12$	1	2

Notice that after 9:
• The units start again at zero.
• 1 in the tens column represents ten.

Try counting in tenths.
Start at 0.7 and keep adding 0.1:

	Tens		Units
$0.7 + 0.1 = 0.8$		•	8
$0.8 + 0.1 = 0.9$		•	9
$0.9 + 0.1 = 1.0$	1	•	0
$1.0 + 0.1 = 1.1$	1	•	1
$1.1 + 0.1 = 1.2$	1	•	2

Notice that after 0.9:
• The tenths start again at zero.
• 1 in the units column represents one.

Example 1

Write down the next two numbers:

1.7   1.8   1.9   ___   ___

Compare with 17   1.7
                  18   1.8
                  19   1.9
                  20   2.0
                  21   2.1

The next two numbers are 2.0 and 2.1

Exercise 8A

Fill in the gaps in each of these sequences.

1   2.6   2.7   2.8   2.9   ____   ____

2   13.5   13.6   13.7   ____   ____   ____

3   4.5   4.6   4.7   4.8   ____   ____

4   99.6   99.7   99.8   ____   ____   ____

8.2 Adding and subtracting decimals

You can add and subtract decimals in the same way you add or subtract sums of money.

Example 2

Add £32.56 and £12.43

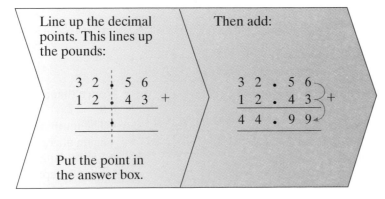

Line up the decimal points. This lines up the pounds:

```
  3 2 . 5 6
  1 2 . 4 3  +
  _____
```

Put the point in the answer box.

Then add:

```
  3 2 . 5 6 ⌉
  1 2 . 4 3 ⌡ +
  _____
  4 4 . 9 9
```

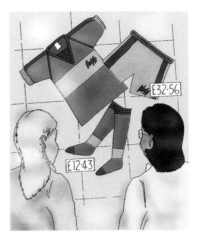

Example 3

Work out £58.54 − £23.26

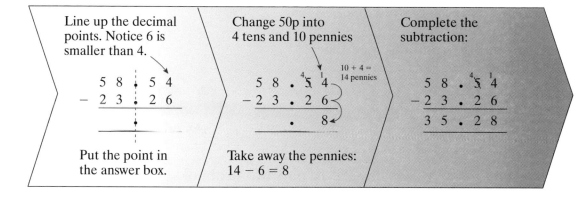

Line up the decimal points. Notice 6 is smaller than 4.

$$5\ 8\ .\ 5\ 4$$
$$-\ 2\ 3\ .\ 2\ 6$$

Put the point in the answer box.

Change 50p into 4 tens and 10 pennies

$$10 + 4 = 14\ \text{pennies}$$

$$5\ 8\ .\ 5\ 4$$
$$-\ 2\ 3\ .\ 2\ 6$$
$$.\ 8$$

Take away the pennies: 14 − 6 = 8

Complete the subtraction:

$$5\ 8\ .\ 5\ 4$$
$$-\ 2\ 3\ .\ 2\ 6$$
$$3\ 5\ .\ 2\ 8$$

■ **To add or subtract decimals:**
   • **line up the decimal points**
   • **put the point in the answer**
   • **add or subtract.**

Exercise 8B

Work these out:

1 (a) £32.53 + £24.05   (b) £5.40 + £14.37
   (c) £2.30 + £7.60   (d) £8.42 + £6.35
   (e) £57.36 + £18.44   (f) £16.39 + £37.24

2 (a) 4.2 + 1.6   (b) 6 + 1.38
   (c) 163.7 + 0.25   (d) 9.2 + 8.3
   (e) 1.3 + 16.2 + 2.46   (f) 8.01 + 15 + 0.52

3 (a) 3.6 + 1.5   (b) 7 + 9.26
   (c) 243.7 + 0.46   (d) 7.8 + 6.4
   (e) 5.7 + 6.2 + 2.4   (f) 6.51 + 14 + 0.73

4 (a) £5.94 − £3.82   (b) £3.49 − £1.26
   (c) £19.65 − £4.23   (d) £14.25 − £8.73

5 (a) 7.8 − 3.4   (b) 0.95 − 0.52
   (c) 3.9 − 0.5   (d) 14.7 − 3.4
   (e) 9.47 − 4.23   (f) 16.86 − 4.35

6 (a) 230.8 − 3.4   (b) 0.92 − 0.56   Hint:
   (c) 2.3 − 0.6   (d) 1 − 0.4   write 1 as 1.0
   (e) 9.2 − 4.7   (f) 15.82 − 2.35

7   Paul ran 1.75 km from West Wood
    to Oakwood, 2.1 km from
    Oakwood to Blackstone and
    2.24 km from Blackstone back to
    West Wood.
    Work out the total distance that
    Paul ran.

8   Jo's empty bag weighs 0.98 kg. Jo puts two textbooks,
    weighing 1.23 kg and 0.94 kg, an exercise book weighing
    0.3 kg and a pencil box weighing 0.34 kg in her bag.
    What is the total weight of Jo's bag and its contents?

9   The temperature in London at noon was 18.3 °C.
    By midnight the temperature had fallen by 5.2 °C.
    What was the temperature in London at midnight?

10 Ramana sawed a length of 0.35 metre from a one
    metre piece of wood. Work out the length of wood left
    over.

8.3 Multiplying and dividing by 10 and 100

You can multiply and divide decimal numbers by 10 and
100 in the same way as whole numbers.

Remember:

■ **Multiplying by 10 moves the** $6 \times 10 = 60$
   digits one place to the left.

■ **Multiplying by 100 moves the** $6 \times 100 = 600$
   digits two places to the left.

■ **Dividing moves the digits to the**
   right:
      $3400 \div 10 = 340$ (1 place)
      $3400 \div 100 = 34$ (2 places)

Example 4

Find:

(a) 63.58×10 (b) 5.94×100 (c) $32.6 \div 10$ (d) $1538.4 \div 100$

Use a place value diagram to help:

(a) Move the digits one place to the left:

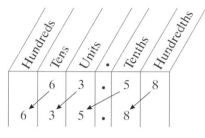

so $63.58 \times 10 = 635.8$

(b) Move the digits 2 places to the left:

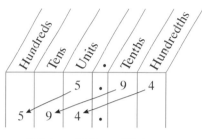

so $5.94 \times 100 = 594$

(c) Move the digits one place to the right:

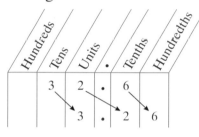

so $32.6 \div 10 = 3.26$

(d) Move the digits 2 places to the right:

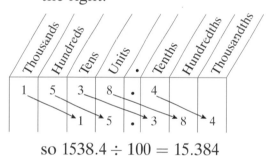

so $1538.4 \div 100 = 15.384$

Exercise 8C

Find:

1 (a) 4.74×10 (b) 23.5×10 (c) 0.503×10 Hint: use a place
   (d) 0.079×10 (e) 67.39×10 (f) 0.04×10 value diagram

2 (a) 5.83×100 (b) 32.59×100 (c) 3.679×100
   (d) 6.49×100 (e) 45.8×100 (f) 0.07×100

3 (a) 0.076×100 (b) 6.408×100 (c) 0.0303×10
   (d) 7.99×100 (e) 8.47×10 (f) 0.0056×10

4 (a) $21.7 \div 10$ (b) $156 \div 10$ (c) $1.63 \div 10$
   (d) $1567.2 \div 10$ (e) $69.5 \div 10$ (f) $0.16 \div 10$

5 (a) $162 \div 100$ (b) $38 \div 100$ (c) $96.7 \div 100$
   (d) $580 \div 100$ (e) $7.4 \div 100$ (f) $1477 \div 100$

8.4 Multiplying decimals by whole numbers

You can also multiply decimals by whole numbers:

Example 5

Find $6 \times £24.31$

Ignore the decimal point:

$$\begin{array}{r} 2431 \\ \times\ 6 \\ \hline 14586 \\ {}^{2\,1} \end{array}$$

The answer 14 586 is in pence. You must put the decimal point back in to get the answer in pounds – £145.86

24.31 has 2 decimal places

so the answer also has 2 decimal places: 145.86

$6 \times £24.31 = £145.86$

■ **To multiply a decimal by a whole number:**
  • **ignore the decimal point**
  • **multiply the numbers**
  • **put the decimal point back in the same place.**

Exercise 8D

1 Find the cost of:
   (a) 5 books at £5.43 each.
   (b) 2 kg of bananas at £0.89 per kg.
   (c) 4 oranges at £0.36 each.
   (d) 6 cards at £1.35 each.

2 Find:
   (a) 4.5×3 (b) 8.7×2 (c) 3.4×6
   (d) 2.46×4 (e) 13.4×5 (f) 7.34×8

3 Find:
   (a) 23.47×5 (b) 6.7×4 (c) 32.64×6
   (d) 6.53×7 (e) 9.52×3 (f) 14.62×9

4 Work out the cost of 3 train tickets which cost £5.65 each.

5   Find the total length, in metres, of 6 tape measures, each 1.52 metres long.

6   Work out the total capacity, in litres, of 4 jugs which each hold 1.4 litres.

Remember:
Always put the units in your answer.

7   Find the total cost of three CDs at £12.30 each and four cassettes at £7.50 each.

8   Calculate the total cost of four bottles of lemonade costing £0.62 each and eight packs of crisps which cost 32p each.

Hint:
Write 32p as £0.32.

8.5 Dividing decimals by whole numbers

Three friends each pay an equal share of the bill for their meal.
The meal costs £23.16. How much do they each pay?

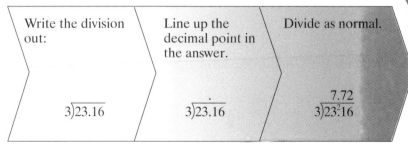

Write the division out:

$3\overline{)23.16}$

Line up the decimal point in the answer.

$3\overline{)23.16}$

Divide as normal.

$3\overline{)23.^216}$ = 7.72

There is more about division on p. 61.

So they each pay £7.72.

■   **To divide a decimal by a whole number:**
    • **line up the decimal point in the answer**
    • **divide as normal.**

Exercise 8E

1   What is each person's share when:
    (a) Three people share £3.96 equally.
    (b) Four people share £16.48 equally.
    (c) Six people share £12.84 equally.
    (d) Seven people share £23.94 equally.

2   Find:
    (a) $86.4 \div 2$ **(b)** $54.6 \div 3$ **(c)** $74.5 \div 5$
    (d) $167.2 \div 4$ **(e)** $98.58 \div 6$ **(f)** $35.76 \div 2$

3 Find:
  (a) $0.684 \div 6$ **(b)** $0.735 \div 7$ **(c)** $1.08 \div 4$
  (d) $7.401 \div 3$ **(e)** $8.04 \div 8$ **(f)** $11.745 \div 9$

4 Three people share the cost of a present equally. The present costs £14.70 How much does each person pay?

5 A piece of rope 61 metres long is used to mark out the perimeter of a square. Work out the length of one side of the square.

8.6 Rounding

It is sometimes useful to round a decimal to the nearest whole number. This can help you check your answers.

37.6
more than 5 round up to 38.

■ **To round to the nearest whole number look at the figure in the first decimal place:**
  • **if it is 5 or more round the whole number up to the next whole number.**
  • **if it is less than 5 do not change the whole number.**

Example 6
Round these decimals to the nearest whole number:
(a) 18.35 **(b)** 2.54 **(c)** 0.76 **(d)** 9.8

(a) 18.35 is between 18 and 19.
  The first decimal place is 3 so round down to 18.

17 18 19 20

(b) 2.54 is between 2 and 3.
  The first decimal place is 5 so round up to 3.

1 2 3 4

(c) 0.76 is between 0 and 1.
  The first decimal place is 7 so round up to 1.

−1 0 1 2

(d) 9.8 is between 9 and 10.
  The first decimal place is 8 so round up to 10.

8 9 10 11

Exercise 8F

Round these decimals to the nearest whole number:

1 **(a)** 5.3 **(b)** 2.9 **(c)** 7.5 **(d)** 8.6

2 **(a)** 15.4 **(b)** 16.7 **(c)** 4.2 **(d)** 29.8

3 **(a)** 0.83 **(b)** 40.27 **(c)** 37.45 **(d)** 200.08

4 **(a)** 36.92 **(b)** 3.9 **(c)** 217.39 **(d)** 59.09

5 **(a)** 7.38 **(b)** 429.7 **(c)** 32 798.6 **(d)** 37.17

6 **(a)** 89.72 **(b)** 0.83 **(c)** 49.29 **(d)** 199.54

Write these answers to the nearest whole number of pounds:

7 **(a)** £5.38 **(b)** 2.76 **(c)** £15.62

8 **(a)** £8.76 **(b)** £0.93 **(c)** £53.73

9 **(a)** £875.51 **(b)** £5326.75 **(c)** £43.62

10 **(a)** £254.49 **(b)** £3627.93 **(c)** £452.89

8.7 Finding approximate answers

You can use rounding to check answers to calculations.

Example 7

Estimate the answer to:

(a) 5.98×2.1 **(b)** $30.87 \div 4.9$ **(c)** $\dfrac{19.73 - 4.815}{1.9}$

(a) Round to whole numbers:

$$5.98 \times 2.1$$
$$\approx 6 \times 2 = 12 \qquad \text{(actual answer 12.558)}$$

$\approx$ means nearly equal to

(b) Round to whole numbers:

$$30.87 \div 4.9$$
$$\approx 31 \div 5$$

This is still not easy so round again:

$$31 \div 5$$
$$\approx 30 \div 5 = 6 \qquad \text{(actual answer 6.2)}$$

(c) Round to whole numbers:

$$\frac{19.73 - 4.81}{1.9}$$
$$\approx \frac{20 - 5}{2} = \frac{15}{2} = 7.5 \qquad \text{(actual answer 7.85)}$$

Exercise 8G

For each question:

(a) estimate the answer using approximate values

(b) work out the exact answer using a calculator.

1 8.93×4 **2** 5.16×6 **3** 19.8×3.1

4 29.94×1.9 **5** $9.12 \div 3$ **6** $31.16 \div 2.05$

7 402.15×3.1 **8** $60.32 \div 5.8$ **9** $89.11 \div 1.9$

10 $\dfrac{29.1 + 40.4}{5}$ **11** $\dfrac{38.2 - 20.6}{4}$ **12** $2.9 \times (4.1 + 5.8)$

13 $\dfrac{71.39 - 40.7}{3.1}$ **14** $\dfrac{40.3 + 21.18}{2.9}$ **15** $\dfrac{90.36 - 9.8}{3.8}$

8.8 Writing decimals in size order

Edward's six javelin throws were:

63.45 m   69.63 m   72.30 m

72.38 m   72.17 m   69.61 m

You can arrange these distances in size order:

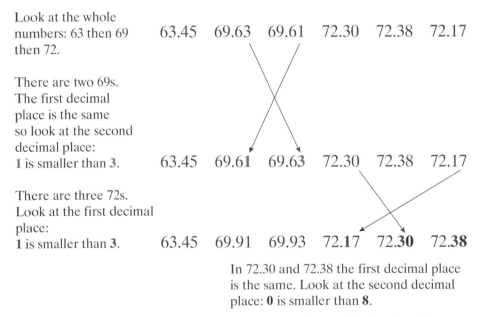

Look at the whole numbers: 63 then 69 then 72.

63.45   69.63   69.61   72.30   72.38   72.17

There are two 69s. The first decimal place is the same so look at the second decimal place: **1** is smaller than **3**.

63.45   69.61   69.63   72.30   72.38   72.17

There are three 72s. Look at the first decimal place: **1** is smaller than **3**.

63.45   69.91   69.93   72.17   72.30   72.38

In 72.30 and 72.38 the first decimal place is the same. Look at the second decimal place: **0** is smaller than **8**.

Now the numbers are in size order, starting with the smallest.

Exercise 8H

Rearrange these numbers in order of size, starting with the largest:

1 0.2, 0.9, 0.4
2 0.02, 0.08, 0.05
3 0.32, 0.7, 0.56
4 0.09, 0.5, 0.34
5 2.4, 3.2, 2.6, 3.1
6 0.32, 0.45, 0.41, 0.39
7 0.52, 0.81, 0.58, 0.85
8 4.6, 5.9, 4.8, 5.2, 5.6
9 4.08, 3.5, 4.05, 4.2, 3.8
10 1.09, 0.08, 1.2, 0.3, 0.16

Put these numbers in size order, smallest first.

11 2.92, 3.58, 3.29, 3.51, 2.78
12 3.24, 1.68, 1.73, 3.09, 3.54
13 3, 7.24, 3.01, 7.08, 3.09
14 0.72, 1.04, 1.1, 0.708, 0.39
15 0.23, 0.08, 0.27, 0.06, 0.3

8.9 Understanding percentages

The symbol % is read as per cent.
Per cent means 'in every 100'.
7% means '7 in every 100'.

7% is called a percentage.

100% means the whole lot.

Hint:
● A century is 100 years.
● A Roman **cent**urion commanded 100 foot soldiers.
● A US dollar is 100 **cent**s.

Example 8

A rectangular cake is cut into five equal pieces.
What percentage is each piece?

The whole cake is 100%
There are 5 pieces.

$100 \div 5 = 20\%$

So each piece is 20% of the whole cake.

Example 9

What percentage of this shape is shaded?.

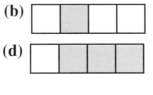

The whole shape is 100%.
It is split into 20 equal parts.
Each part is 100% ÷ 20 = 5%.

3 parts are shaded.
So 3 × 5% is shaded.
15% of the shape is shaded.

Exercise 8I

1   Debbie saws a plank of wood into four equal pieces.
    What percentage of the plank is each piece?

2   What percentage of each shape is shaded?

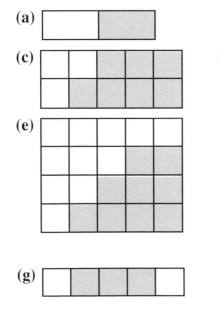

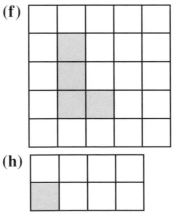

8.10 Percentages as fractions

You can also write percentages as fractions.

13% means 13 in every 100. So $13\% = \dfrac{13}{100}$

- **A percentage can be written as a fraction with denominator (bottom) 100.**

  For example, $7\% = \dfrac{7}{100}$

Example 10

60% of Year 8 students watched the big football match on TV. What fraction of the students watched the match?

Write 60% as a fraction in its simplest form.

$$60\% \;=\; \overset{\div 20}{\underset{\div 20}{\frac{60}{100}}} \;=\; \frac{3}{5}$$

Remember:
A fraction is in its **simplest form** when there is no equivalent fraction with smaller numbers on the top or bottom.

$\frac{60}{100}$ simplifies to $\frac{3}{5}$ so $\frac{3}{5}$ of Year 8 students watched the match.

Example 11

Write $66\frac{2}{3}\%$ as a fraction in its simplest form.

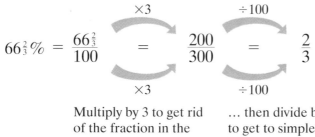

$$66\tfrac{2}{3}\% \;=\; \overset{\times 3}{\underset{\times 3}{\frac{66\frac{2}{3}}{100}}} \;=\; \overset{\div 100}{\underset{\div 100}{\frac{200}{300}}} \;=\; \frac{2}{3}$$

Multiply by 3 to get rid of the fraction in the numerator …

… then divide by 100 to get to simplest form.

So $66\tfrac{2}{3}\% = \tfrac{2}{3}$

Exercise 8J

1   Change these percentages to fractions.

(a) 41%   (b) 39%   (c) 3%   (d) 27%

(e) 21%   (f) 17%   (g) 63%   (h) 19%

(i) 9%   (j) 51%   (k) 13%   (l) 99%

2   Change these percentages to fractions in their lowest terms.

Lowest terms means the same as simplest form.

(a) 40%   (b) 45%   (c) 80%   (d) 10%

(e) 44%   (f) 25%   (g) 30%   (h) 24%

(i) 32%   (j) 36%   (k) 75%   (l) 4%

3   Change these percentages to fractions in their simplest form.

(a) 1%   (b) 28%   (c) 14%   (d) 5%

(e) 48%   (f) 90%   (g) 16%   (h) 35%

(i) $2\frac{1}{2}\%$ (j) $17\frac{1}{2}\%$ (k) $33\frac{1}{3}\%$ (l) $16\frac{2}{3}\%$

4   In a sale all the prices are reduced by $12\frac{1}{2}\%$. Write $12\frac{1}{2}\%$ as a fraction in its lowest terms.

5   The interest on a loan is 8% each year. Write 8% as a fraction in its simplest form.

8.11 Converting percentages to decimals

You can also write a percentage as a decimal.

3% means $\frac{3}{100}$.

To change $\frac{3}{100}$ to a decimal, divide the numerator by the denominator:

$$\frac{3}{100} = 3 \div 100 = 0.03$$

so 3% in decimal form is 0.03.

■   **To write a percentage as a decimal you divide by 100.**

   For example, $62\% = \dfrac{62}{100} = 62 \div 100 = 0.62$

Exercise 8K

1   Change these percentages to decimals:

   (a) 16%   (b) 39%   (c) 63%   (d) 95%
   (e) 4%   (f) 37%   (g) 26%   (h) 3%
   (i) 35%   (j) 1%   (k) 6%   (l) 71%
   (m) 23%   (n) 27%   (o) 12%   (p) 60%

2   Copy and complete this table of equivalent percentages, fractions and decimals.

What does equivalent mean:

50% $\frac{1}{2}$ 0.5

are three different ways of writing the same number.

Percentage	Fraction	Decimal
50%	$\frac{1}{2}$	0.5
30%		
	$\frac{1}{4}$	
75%		
	$\frac{1}{10}$	
$66\frac{2}{3}$%		
20%		
	$\frac{1}{3}$	

These are common percentages. You should try and recognise them and their equivalent fractions and decimals.

Hint:
If you divide 2 by 3 on your calculator, the answer is 0.666...
You write this as $0.\dot{6}$
You say 'nought point six recurring'.

8.12 Finding a percentage of an amount

■   **To find a percentage of an amount:**
   ● **change the percentage to a decimal**
   ● **multiply the decimal by the number**

Example 12

15% of the pupils in a school live over 20 minutes walk away.
The school has 400 pupils.
How many of them live over 20 minutes walk away?

You need to find 15% of 400 pupils.

To find 15% of 400 pupils:

- change 15% to a decimal:

$$\frac{15}{100} = \quad 15 \div 100 \quad = \quad 0.15$$

- multiply 0.15 by 400:

$$0.15 \times 400 = 60$$

so 15% of 400 pupils is 60 pupils.

> Remember:
> 15% means 15 in every hundred:
>
> | 100 | 100 | 100 | 100 |
>
> $15 + 15 + 15 + 15 = 60$
>
> You can use this shortcut with all multiples of 100.

Exercise 8L

1. Find:
   - **(a)** 30% of 400 pupils
   - **(b)** 25% of 600 pupils
   - **(c)** 15% of 300 litres.

> Hint:
> In percentage questions 'of' always means 'multiply':
>
> 30% of 400
>
> means 30% × 400

2. Work out:
   - **(a)** 20% of £400
   - **(b)** 15% of 500 metres
   - **(c)** 35% of 700 students.

3. There are 48 people in a swimming pool.
   25% of them have a blue armband.
   How many people have a blue armband?

4. A tutor group raised £135.
   They gave 60% of the money to charity.
   How much did they give to charity?

5. In a sale all marked prices were reduced by 15%.
   What is the sale price of a shirt that was originally priced at £19?

6. Work out:
   - **(a)** 10% of £5
   - **(b)** 20% of £45
   - **(c)** 50% of £13
   - **(d)** 25% of £32
   - **(e)** 75% of £28
   - **(f)** 30% of £50
   - **(g)** 12% of £26
   - **(h)** 15% of £36
   - **(i)** 80% of £15

7. Work out:
   - **(a)** 3% of £25
   - **(b)** 6% of £70
   - **(c)** 5% of £34
   - **(d)** 4% of 15 m
   - **(e)** 5% of 42 m
   - **(f)** 35% of 18 kg
   - **(g)** 2% of 19 kg
   - **(h)** 3% of 35 kg
   - **(i)** 8% of 27.5 kg

8.13 Increasing and decreasing by a percentage

Price increases and decreases are usually given in percentages. You can work out the new price by finding the price increase or decrease.

SALE
20% off
all marked prices

Example 13

A shop puts up its prices by 5%.
What is the new price of a TV that used to cost £240?

The price increase is 5% of £240

$$= 0.05 \times £240$$

$$= £12$$

Remember:
0.05 is the decimal
equivalent of 5%

So the new price = old price + increase

$$= £240 + £12$$

$$= £252$$

Example 14

In a sale there is 20% off all marked prices.
What is the sale price of a shirt marked £40?

The price decrease is 20% of £40

$$= 0.2 \times £40$$

$$= £8$$

So the sale price = original price − decrease

$$= £40 − £8 = £32$$

■ **To find the value after a percentage change:**
  • **work out the increase then add it to the original or**
  • **work out the decrease then subtract it from the original.**

Exercise 8M

1 Gemma earns £165 a week working at a supermarket.
   She is given a 3% pay rise. Work out:
   (a) the amount of her pay rise
   (b) how much she now earns each week.

2   At the beginning of a year the minimum bus fare in a city was 80 pence. At the end of the year this increased by 5%. What was the minimum bus fare at the end of the year?

3   In a sale a shop reduced the prices of all CDs by 15%. For a CD usually costing £12, work out:

   (a) the reduction in price

   (b) the sale price.

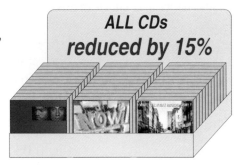

4   In September 1999 the number of pupils in Year 8 at a school was 125. In February 2000 that number had increased by 4%. How many pupils were in Year 8 at the school in February 2000?

5   Rosina buys a new car for £9600. After 3 years it loses 40% of its value. Work out the value of the car after 3 years.

6   In January a factory employed 400 workers. By May the number of workers had increased by 5%. How many workers were employed in May?

7   A travel agency offers a discount of 12% off a holiday usually costing £250. What is the new cost of the holiday?

8   Last year Harjit's water rates were £220. The rates have risen by 6%. What are his water rates now?

9   In a sale all the usual prices were reduced by 20%. Work out the sale price of a sweater usually priced at £26.

10   Find the new amount when:

   (a) £45 is increased by 6%

   (b) £38 is decreased by 4%

   (c) £154 is increased by 17%

   (d) 60 kg is decreased by 8%

   (e) 156 litres is increased by 5%

   (f) 2.5 kg is decreased by 16%.

8.14 Writing one quantity as a percentage of another

You can write one amount as a percentage of another amount.

Example 15

Helen scored 42 out of 60 in a test.
What was her percentage score?

Step 1: Write the quantities as a fraction: $\dfrac{42}{60}$

Step 2: Change the fraction to a decimal: $42 \div 60 = 0.7$

Step 3: Multiply by 100%: $0.7 \times 100\%$
$= 70\%$

Helen's mark was 70%.

> Remember: to multiply by 100 move the digits two places to the left.

■ **To write one quantity as a percentage of another:**
  ● **write the quantities as a fraction**
  ● **change the fraction to a decimal**
  ● **multiply by 100%**

Exercise 8N

1 The top mark in a test was 69 out of 75. Write this as a percentage.

2 There are 60 cars in the staff car park and 24 of them are red. What percentage of the cars are red?

3 A business employs 360 people and 54 of them are given a long service award. What percentage of the employees are given the award?

4 Out of 80 peaches in a tray, 12 are bad. What percentage of the peaches are bad?

5 In a class of 30 pupils 18 are girls. What percentage of the class are (a) girls, (b) boys?

6 Syreeta has 450 stamps and 18 of them are Chinese. What percentage of her stamps are Chinese?

7 Of the 150 pupils in Year 8, 108 usually walk to school. Work out the percentage of Year 8 pupils who usually walk to school.

8 Barry bought 35 flower plants and 28 of them had pink flowers. What percentage of the plants had pink flowers?

9 A group of 450 runners took part in a marathon and 432 of the group finished. What percentage of the group finished?

10 Write:

(a) £1.62 as a percentage of £4.50.
(b) 24 g as a percentage of 80 g
(c) 38 cm as a percentage of 2 m
(d) 280 g as a percentage of 4 kg

Hint: change 2 m into cm first.

Change 4 kg to g first.

Summary of key points

1 In a decimal number the decimal point separates the whole number from the part that is less than one.

2 To add or subtract decimals
- line up the decimal points
- put the point in the answer
- add or subtract.

3 Remember:
Multiplying by 10 moves the digits one place to the left. $6 \times 10 = 60$

Multiplying by 100 moves the digits two places to the left. $6 \times 100 = 600$

Dividing moves the digits to the right:
$3400 \div 10 = 340$ (1 place)
$3400 \div 100 = 34$ (2 places)

4 To multiply a decimal by a whole number:
- ignore the decimal point
- multiply the numbers
- put the decimal point back in the same place.

5 To divide a decimal by a whole number:
- line up the decimal point in the answer
- divide as normal.

6 To round the nearest whole number look at the figure in the first decimal place:
- if it is 5 or more round the whole number up
- if it is less than 5 do not change the whole number.

7 A percentage can be written as a fraction with a denominator (bottom) 100.

For example, $7\% = \dfrac{7}{100}$

8 To write a percentage as a decimal you divide by 100.

For example, $62\% = \dfrac{62}{100} = 62 \div 100 = 0.62$

9 To find the value after a percentage change:
- work out the increase then add it to the original
or
- work out the decrease then subtract it from the original.

10 To write one quantity as a fraction of another:
- write the quantity as a fraction of the other
- change the fraction to a decimal
- multiply by 100%.

9 Shape and measure

Architects use shapes to create stylish effects on buildings.

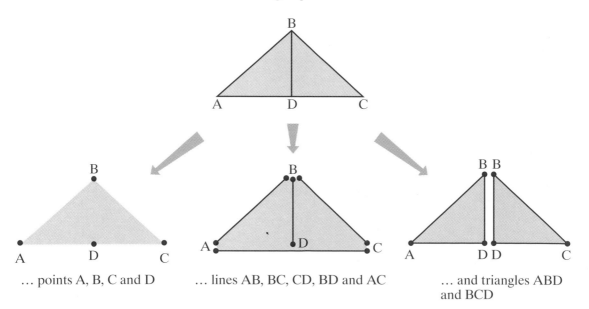

9.1 Name that shape

You can use letters to describe points, lines and shapes:

This triangle splits into …

… points A, B, C and D   … lines AB, BC, CD, BD and AC   … and triangles ABD and BCD

Example 1

Name all the points, lines and shapes in this diagram:

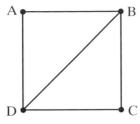

Points: A, B, C, D

Lines: AB, BC, CD, DA, DB

Shapes: triangle ABD
          triangle BCD
          square ABCD

Sketching these
helps you avoid
double counting:

Exercise 9A

1   List all the points, lines and shapes in these diagrams:

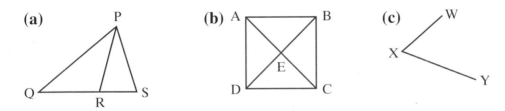

(a)   **(b)**   **(c)**

2   List the triangles in each diagram:

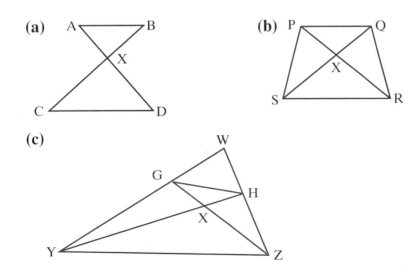

(a)   **(b)**

(c)

3 For each diagram list pairs of:
- parallel lines
- perpendicular lines.

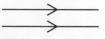

(a)

(b)

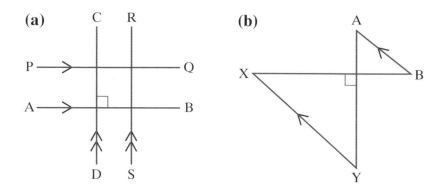

4 Follow these instructions to sketch triangle ABC.
- Point A is at the bottom left-hand corner.
- Line AB goes 2 cm vertically up the page.
- Line AC goes 2 cm horizontally to the right.

5 Use these instructions to sketch OPQ:
- Draw point O.
- Line OP goes 2 cm to the right of point O.
- Line PQ goes vertically up from P by 2 cm.
- Angle OPQ is 90°.

6 Copy and complete this diagram:

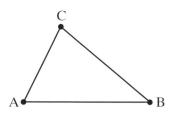

- Draw a line through C which is parallel to AB.
- Draw in point D so that line CD is the same length as AB and line BD is parallel to AC.
- Line BD should be the same length as AC.

9.2 Special quadrilaterals and triangles

This table will remind you of some special quadrilaterals and triangles and their properties:

Shape	Name	Properties
	Square	All sides equal All angles equal
	Rectangle	Opposite sides equal All angles equal
	Rhombus	All sides equal Opposite angles equal
	Kite	Two pairs of adjacent sides equal One pair of opposite angles equal
	Parallelogram	Opposite sides equal and parallel Opposite angles equal
	Isosceles triangle	Two sides equal Two angles equal
	Equalateral triangle	All sides equal Opposite angles equal
	Scalene triangle	No sides equal No angles equal

Lines marked ─┼─ or ─╫─ are equal.
Lines marked ─›─ or ─»─ are parallel.

■ **The diagonals of special quadrilaterals also have special properties:**

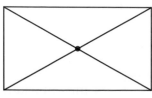

The diagonals of a rectangle are the same length and meet at the centre.

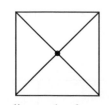

The diagonals of a square bisect each other at right angles.

bi means 2.
bisect means cut in half.

(Think of disect which means cut in pieces).

Activity

Investigate the properties of the diagonals in the shapes on Activity Sheet 1.

● Measure lengths and angles.
● Comment on what you notice.

Exercise 9B

1   Copy and complete these sentences:

  (a) The opposite sides of a parallelogram are

  _____ and _____

  (b) A square has _____ sides. The

  diagonals _____ each other at _____

  (c) When the diagonals of a kite cross they make

  a _____

  (d) All _____ of a rhombus are equal. The

  diagonals _____ at right angles.

  (e) An _____ triangle has three equal sides and

  angles.

  (f) A scalene triangle has _____ equal sides

  and _____ equal angles.

2 Identify as many different shapes as you can in this diagram. Use letters to describe them, and write their mathematical names.

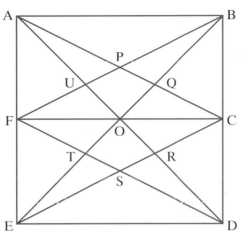

Hint:
Use the table on p. 139 to help.

3 Four equal kites make the star with points at P, Q, R and S. Its centre is at X. Explain why ABCD and PQRS are squares.

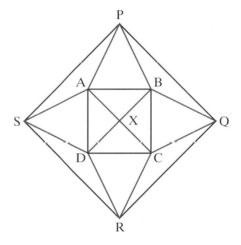

9.3 Circles

There are special names for some parts of a circle:

■ The **circumference** is the perimeter of the circle.

■ **A diameter is a straight line through the centre from one point on the circumference to another.**

■ **A radius is a straight line from the centre to the circumference. It is half the length of a diameter.**

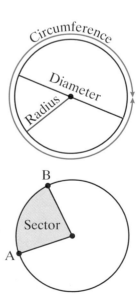

■ **An arc is any part of the circumference, this is arc AB.**

■ **A sector is any area made by two radius lines and part of the circumference.**

Exercise 9C

1   Name a radius, diameter, sector, and arc in this diagram.

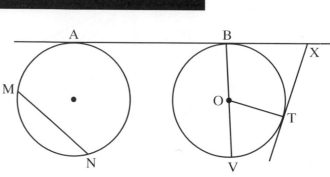

2   The diagram shows two intersecting circles. QA is a radius of the circle with centre Q. P is the centre of the other circle.

Name the other radiuses.

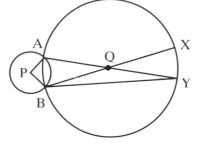

Hint: intersecting means 'crossing over'.

Any circle has an infinite number of radiuses or radii (pronounced ray-dee-eye).

9.4 Constructing shapes

You can use a ruler and compasses to help you draw shapes accurately.
An accurate drawing like this is called a **construction**.

Example 2

Construct this shape with ruler and compasses.

Use the ruler to set the compasses at 3 cm. Leave them set like this throughout.

First draw a circle …

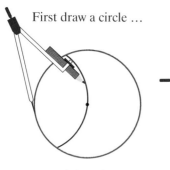

… and draw in an arc through the centre.

Draw in these arcs:

follow the pattern …

… until you end up with this shape.

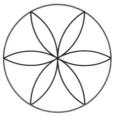

Exercise 9D

1   Construct these designs using a ruler and compass.

(a)

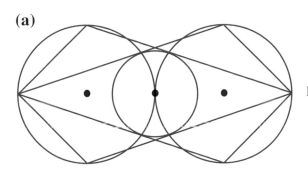

Hint: The small circle is drawn last.

(b)

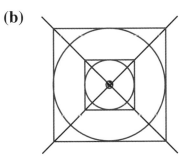

Hint: Draw the cross and work from the inside.

(c)

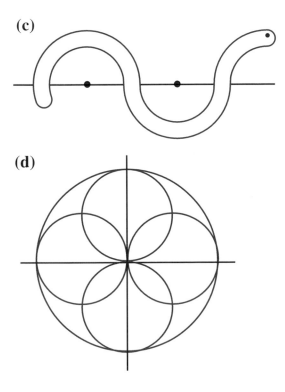

(d)

9.5 Solids

You need to be able to recognize these common solids.

Name:	Shape:	Properties:
Cuboid		6 rectangular faces
Cube		6 square faces
Square-based pyramid		Base is square. It has 4 triangular sides.
Prism		Any shape with a constant cross-section
Cylinder		A prism with a constant circular cross-section.
Cone		A pyramid with a circular base.
Sphere		The shape of a ball
Hemisphere		Half a sphere.

Remember:
Each surface is
called a **face**.

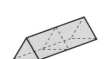

A prism is the same
shape all the way
through.

Exercise 9E

1 For each picture give the mathematical name of the shapes which make these solids.

Hint:
(**a**) is a square-based pyramid and a cuboid.

(a)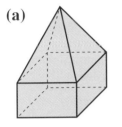

(b)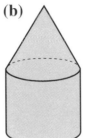

(c)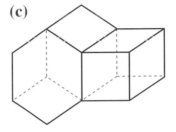

(d)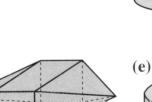

(e)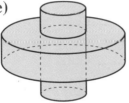

(f)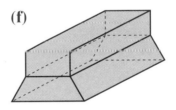

(g)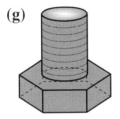

(h)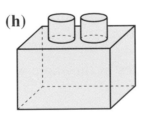

(i)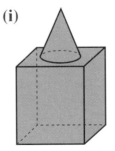

(j)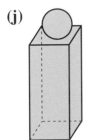

(k)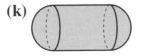

Different solid shapes have different numbers of **faces**, **edges** and **vertices**.

■ **A face is one surface of a solid.**

■ **An edge is the line where two faces meet.**

■ **A vertex is the point where three or more edges meet.**

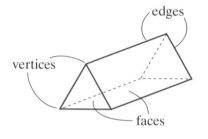

Vertex is the mathematical name for a **corner**.

Plural: vertices

Example 3

How many faces, edges and vertices are there on this cuboid?

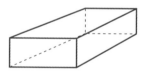

There are 6 faces, 12 edges and 8 vertices.

You can name faces, edges and vertices in the same way as you name angles, lines and shapes.

Example 4

Name all the faces, edges and vertices in this square-based pyramid.

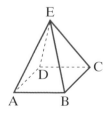

Faces: ABE, BCE, CDE, DAE and ABCD.

Edges: AB, BC, CD, DA, AE, BE, CE and DE.

Vertices: A, B, C, D and E.

Exercise 9F

1 **Activity**. Copy and complete this table. (Hint: use the shapes on page 144 to help you.)

Name	Faces	Edges	Vertices
Cuboid	6	12	8
Cube			
Square-based pyramid			
Prism			
Cylinder			
Cone			

2 In this cuboid name:

(a) two vertical faces
(b) a horizontal edge
(c) two perpendicular edges
(d) the vertex behind point A
(e) two parallel faces
(f) a vertical diagonal face

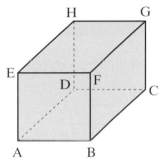

3 For this shape, name:
(a) an edge which is parallel to BC
(b) all the faces which are perpendicular to ADEB
(c) all the edges which are parallel to AD
(d) all the edges which are perpendicular to AD

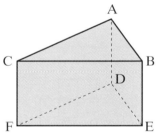

9.6 Nets

You can fold this
2-dimensional shape …

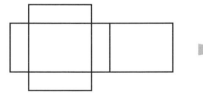

… to make this
3-dimensional cuboid.

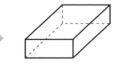

You can describe:
● a flat (2-dimensional) shape using measurement in just 2 directions

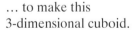

● a solid (3-dimensional) shape using measurements in just 3 directions:

■ **A 2-dimensional shape that is folded to make a 3-dimensional shape is called a *net*.**

Example 5

What does the net of a cube look like?

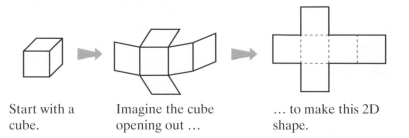

Start with a
cube.

Imagine the cube
opening out …

… to make this 2D
shape.

The 2D shape that you get is the net of the cube.

Exercise 9G

1   Draw these nets on squared paper and see which of
    them can be made into a cube.

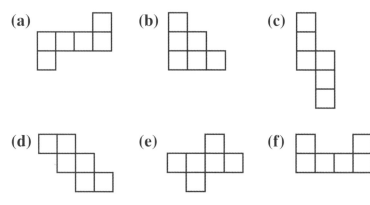

(a)   (b)   (c)

(d)   (e)   (f)

2   Draw a sketch of the shape each of these nets will make:

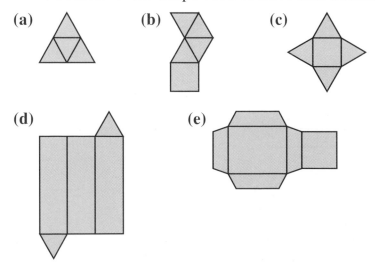

(a)   (b)   (c)

(d)   (e)

9.7 Plan and elevation

■ **The plan of a solid is the two-dimensional view when seen from above.**

■ **The front elevation is the view from the front.**

■ **The side elevation is the view from the side.**

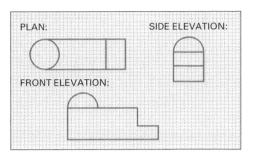

Example 6

Draw the plan and elevations of this square-based pyramid.

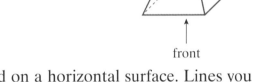

Imagine the pyramid on a horizontal surface. Lines you cannot see are dotted.

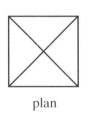
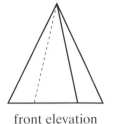
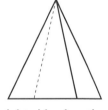

plan   front elevation   right-side elevation

Example 7

Draw the plan and elevation of these three cubes.

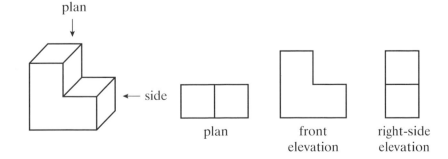

plan   front elevation   right-side elevation

Exercise 9H

1 **Activity:** For each of these plan and elevation descriptions:

- Make the solid (each one uses four cubes)
- Draw the solid using Activity Sheet 2.
  (The first one has been drawn for you).

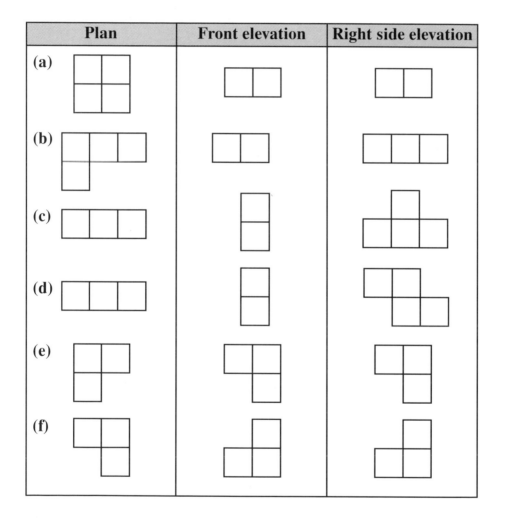

Plan	Front elevation	Right side elevation
(a)		
(b)		
(c)		
(d)		
(e)		
(f)		

2 Draw the plans and elevations of these shapes.

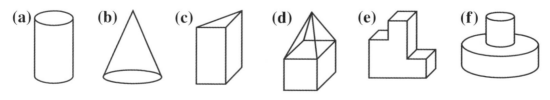

(a)   (b)   (c)   (d)   (e)   (f)

9.8 Measuring lengths and weights

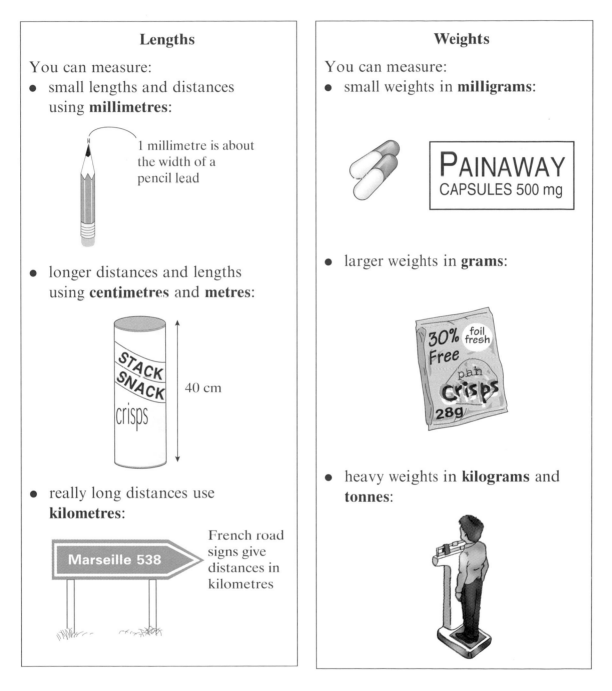

Lengths

You can measure:

- small lengths and distances using **millimetres**:

  1 millimetre is about the width of a pencil lead

- longer distances and lengths using **centimetres** and **metres**:

  STACK SNACK crisps   40 cm

- really long distances use **kilometres**:

  Marseille 538

  French road signs give distances in kilometres

Weights

You can measure:

- small weights in **milligrams**:

  PAINAWAY CAPSULES 500 mg

- larger weights in **grams**:

  30% Free foil fresh p.h.n Crisps 28g

- heavy weights in **kilograms** and **tonnes**:

You can convert lengths and weights into different units:

1 cm = 10 mm   1 g = 1000 mg
1 m = 100 cm   1 kg = 1000 g
1 km = 1000 m   1 t = 1000 kg

Example 8

(a) Convert 358 mm into cm.   (b) Convert 7.2 g into mg.

(a)   1 cm = 10 mm   (b)   1 g = 1000 mg

$$358\,\text{mm} = \frac{358}{10}\,\text{cm}$$

$$7.2\,\text{g} = 7.2 \times 1000$$
$$= 7200\,\text{mg}$$

$$= 35.8\,\text{cm}$$

Exercise 9I

1   Measure these lines to the nearest mm.

(a) _____

(b) _____

(c) _____

(d) _____

(e) _____

(f) _____

2   Draw lines that are:
   (a) 25 mm   (b) 75 mm   (c) 62 mm long.

3   Write in cm:
   (a) 20 mm   (b) 50 mm   (c) 65 mm
   (d) 248 mm   (e) 350 mm   (f) 253 mm

4   Write in mm:
   (a) 3 cm   (b) 8 cm   (c) 7.6 cm
   (d) 18.1 cm   (e) 4.65 cm   (f) 27.6 cm

5   Write in kg:
   (a) 4500 g   (b) 250 g   (c) 500 g   (d) 35 g
   (e) 1050 g   (f) 745 g   (g) 805 g   (h) 2005 g

6   Write in g:
   (a) 6 kg   (b) 5.5 kg   (c) 2.250 kg (d) 0.125 kg
   (e) 3.055 g (f) 80.050 kg (g) 1.243 kg (h) 0.010 kg

9.9 Capacity

■ **Capacity is a measure of the space inside a hollow object.**

You can measure capacity in:

Litres (l)   centilitres (cl)   millilitres (ml)

This bottle holds   This bottle holds   A teaspoon holds
one litre of cola.   70 centilitres of bubble bath. 5 millilitres of medicine.

1 litre = 100 centilitres = 1000 millilitres

Example 9

A glass holds 15 cl. How many glasses can be filled from a
3 litre bottle?

$$3 \, l = 3000 \, ml$$
$$15 \, cl = 150 \, ml$$

So, number of glasses filled $= \dfrac{3000}{150} = 20$

Answer: 20 glasses

Exercise 9J

1   Write as millilitres:
   (a) 5 cl   **(b)** 20 cl   **(c)** 2 litres   **(d)** 5 litres
   (e) 21 litres **(f)** 25 cl   **(g)** 45 cl   **(h)** 50 cl
   (i) 2.5 l   **(j)** $\frac{1}{2}$ l   **(k)** 73 cl   **(l)** 3.1 l

2   Write as litres:
   (a) 5000 ml   **(b)** 3500 ml   **(c)** 4500 ml   **(d)** 500 cl
   (e) 3000 cl   **(f)** 250 cl   **(g)** 500 ml   **(h)** 20 500 ml

3   Put these containers in order of size:

(a)

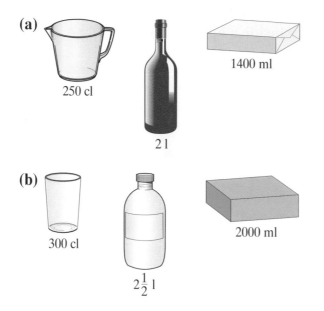

250 cl

2 l

1400 ml

(b)

300 cl

$2\frac{1}{2}$ l

2000 ml

4   Ben tips seventeen 40 cl containers of water into a
20 litre tank. How many more containers must he
empty into the tank to fill it?

9.10 Metric and Imperial measures

So far you have only looked at
measurements made in **metric** units.

You sometimes need to convert metric
units into old-style **Imperial** units such
as miles, pints or pounds:

Metric		**Imperial**
8 kilometres	=	5 miles
1 kilogram	=	2.2 pounds
1 litre	=	1.75 pints

So that's 5 gallons of petrol at 64.2p per litre

Example 10

The distance from London to Carlisle is 300 miles.
How far is it in kilometres?

$$5 \text{ miles} = 8 \text{ kilometres}$$
$$1 \text{ mile} = 8 \div 5 \text{ kilometres}$$
$$300 \text{ miles} = 300 \times (8 \div 5) \text{ km} = 480 \text{ km}$$

Example 11

Nathan weighs 72 kg. What is his weight in pounds?

lb is short for 'libra'
a latin word for
pound.

$$1 \, \text{kg} = 2.2 \text{ pounds (lb)}$$
$$72 \, \text{kg} = 72 \times 2.2 = 158.4 \, \text{lb}$$

Exercise 9K

1   Change these distances to kilometres:
    (a) 40 miles   **(b)** 55 miles   **(c)** 320 miles
    (d) 28 miles   **(e)** 124 miles   **(f)** 236 miles
    (g) 31 miles   **(h)** 103 miles   **(i)** 427 miles

2   Change these distances to miles:
    (a) 40 km   **(b)** 56 km   **(c)** 320 km
    (d) 28 km   **(e)** 124 km   **(f)** 236 km
    (g) 100 km   **(h)** 1000 km   **(i)** 730 km

3   Change into lb (pounds):
    (a) 10 kg   **(b)** 24 kg
    (c) 80 kg   **(d)** 75 kg

4   Change into kg:
    (a) 44 lb   **(b)** 200 lb
    (c) 80 lb   **(d)** 19 lb

5   Change into pints:
    (a) 4 litres   **(b)** 7 litres
    (c) 15 litres   **(d)** 12.5 litres

6   Change into litres:
    (a) 3.5 pints   **(b)** 21 pints
    (c) 8 pints   **(d)** 56 pints

9.11 Time

You should be able to use 12-hour and 24-hour clock times.

Half past two in the morning
12-hour clock   24-hour clock
2 : 30 am   02 : 30

Half past two in the afternoon
12-hour clock   24-hour clock
2 : 30 pm   14 : 30

To get a 24-hour clock time you add on 12 to the hours.
Times between midnight and 1 am start with 00:

12-hour clock	24-hour clock
12 : 15 am	00 : 15
4 : 27 pm	16 : 27

Remember:
am means before midday
pm means after midday

Example 12

School finishes at 15 : 40.

Tea is at 18 : 15.

How much time is there between school and dinner?

From 15 : 40 it takes 20 minutes to reach 16 : 00

It takes another 2 hours to reach 18 : 00

It takes another 15 minutes to reach 18 : 15

Total time is 20 minutes + 2 hours + 15 minutes = 2 hours 35 minutes

Example 13

It is 9:40.

What will the time be in $3\frac{1}{2}$ hours?

You can do the $\frac{1}{2}$ hour first.

In 30 minutes it will be 10:10

In another 3 hours it will be 13:10

Exercise 9L

1   Write the time 1 hour 30 minutes after:
    (a) 07:30   (b) 09:45   (c) 11:50
    (d) 15:35   (e) 18:40   (f) 22:45

2   A TV programme starts at 19:50 and finishes at 22:10. How long is the programme?

3   One morning Jane spends 25 minutes watching TV, 50 minutes listening to music and 1 hour 50 minutes reading. How long has she spent altogether?

4   The central heating is set to come on at 06:45 and go off at 09:15. It then comes on again at 16:30 and stays on until 23:15.
    How long is it on each day? How long is it on for one week?

5   Here is part of a bus timetable.

Hertford	0730	0850	0940	1440	1555	1750
Hoddesdon	0745	0906	0956	1456	1611	1806
Nazeing	0759	0919	1009	1509	1624	1819
Harlow	0820	0942	1028	1531	1645	1841

   (a) How long does the 1555 from Hertford take to get to Nazeing?
   (b) Write down the time the first bus leaves Hoddesdon. How long does it take to reach Harlow?
   (c) How long does the last bus take to get from Hertford to Harlow?

Summary of key points

1   The circumference is the perimeter of the circle.

2   The diameter is a straight line that passes through the centre of a circle.

3   The radius is the distance from the centre to the circumference. It is half the diameter.

4   An arc is any part of the circumference.

5   A sector is any area made by two radius lines and part of the circumference.

6   A face is one surface of a solid.

7   An edge is the line where two faces meet.

8   A vertex is the point where three or more edges meet.

9   A 2-dimensional shape that is folded to make a 3-dimensional shape is called a *net*.

10   The plan of a solid is the two-dimensional view when seen from above.

11   The front elevation is the view from the front.

12   The side elevation is the view from the side.

13   Capacity is a measure of the space inside a hollow object.

10 Positive and negative numbers

10.1 Ordering numbers

An aeroplane is flying over Pakistan:

At 30 000 ft when the outside air temperature is −45°C you can see vapour trails.

For comfort the air is kept at 18°C inside the plane.

On the ground the air temperature is 31°C – quite hot!

■ **Positive numbers are greater than zero. They are sometimes written with a plus sign, e.g. +4 or 4.**

■ **Negative numbers are less than zero. They are written with a minus sign, e.g. −3.**

You can use a number line to help with positive and negative numbers. Number lines can be:

Horizontal ...

... or vertical

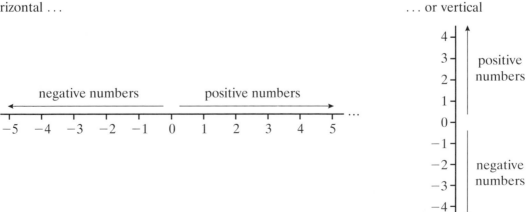

Example 1

On this weather map the numbers are temperatures in degrees Celsius.

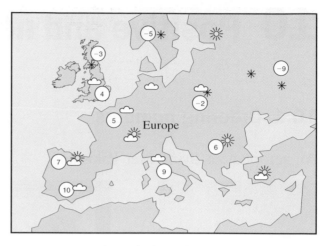

Write down:

(a) the highest temperature.
(b) the lowest temperature.
(c) all the temperatures in order of size, starting with the highest.

A vertical number line may help.

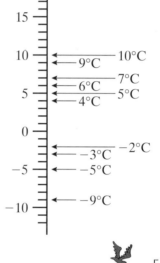

(a) The highest temperature is **10°C**.
(b) The lowest temperature is **−9°C**.
(c) The temperatures in order are
10°C, 9°C, 7°C, 6°C, 5°C, 4°C, −2°C, −3°C, −5°C, −9°C.

Example 2

Alrik and Jane are doing research on dolphins. Jane is in the water.
Alrik sits on the deck.

(a) How many metres above sea level is the top of Alrik's head?
(b) What is at −6 m?
(c) How far above Jane is the bird?

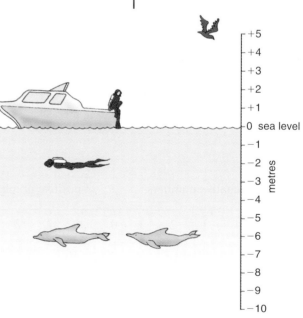

(a) The top of Alrik's head is 2 m above sea level.
(b) The dolphins are at −6 m.
(c) The bird is 7 m above Jane.

Exercise 10A

1 This weather map shows
temperatures in the USA
in °C.
Write down:
  (a) the highest temperature
  (b) the lowest temperature
  (c) all the temperatures in
     order of size, starting
     with the lowest.

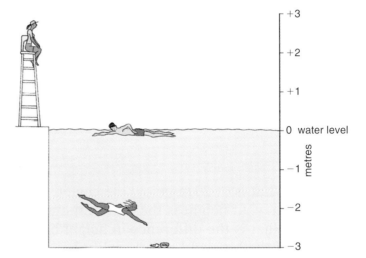

2 Krista has lost her locker
key in the pool.
Write down the height
from the water level of:
  (a) the lifeguard's cap
  (b) Krista
  (c) the other swimmer
  (d) the locker key

3 Here are the buttons that operate a lift.
  (a) Jamal gets in the lift at the car park
     and goes up five floors.
     Which floor does he get out at?
  (b) Jonathan gets in the lift at the fourth
     floor and goes to the basement.
     How many floors does he go down?
  (c) Ceris gets in the lift at the basement
     and goes up two floors.
     Which floor does she get out at?

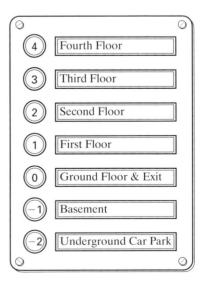

4 Write down these temperatures in order of size, starting with the lowest.
(a) −6°, −2°, −4°, −3°, −8°, 9°.
(b) 5°, −2°, 3°, −6°, −5°, −8°.
(c) −6°, 0°, −4°, −7°, −5°, −3°.
(d) −6°, −4°, −7°, −1°, 3°, −9°.

5

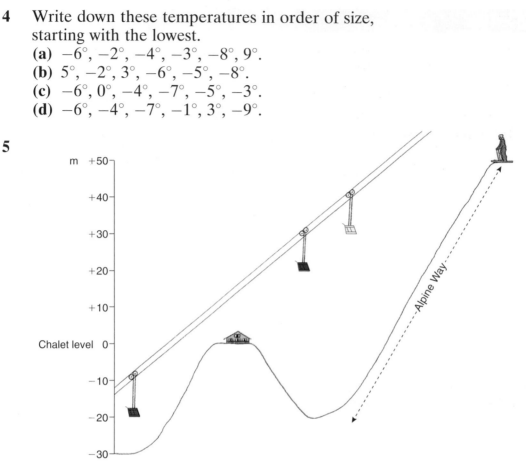

(a) What is at 20 m below the chalet?
(b) At what height is the seat of the yellow chair lift?
(c) What is the difference in height between the seats of the blue and red chair lifts?
(d) The skier at 50 m skies to the bottom of Alpine Way. How far did she go down?

10.2 Using a horizontal number line

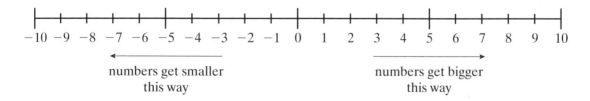

■ **You can use a horizontal number line to answer questions about positive and negative numbers. The smallest number is always on the left.**

Example 3

Use a horizontal number line to find the number that is:
(a) 3 more than −7   **(b)** 5 less than 3.

(a) If you have 3 more, the number gets bigger so you move to the right. Start at −7 and move three spaces to the right. The answer is −4.

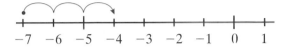

(b) If you have 5 less, the number gets smaller so you move to the left. Start at 3 and move five spaces to the left. The answer is −2.

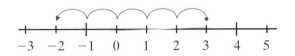

Exercise 10B

1 Use a number line to find the number that is:
    (a) 4 more than 2   **(b)** 5 more than −2
    (c) 3 less than −2   **(d)** 5 less than −4
    (e) 7 more than −2   **(f)** 4 less than 0
    (g) 8 more than −5   **(h)** 4 more than −3
    (i) 8 more than −8   **(j)** 8 more than −2
    (k) 4 more than −9   **(l)** 7 more than −3

2 What number is:
    (a) 3 more than −9   **(b)** 3 less than −5
    (c) 7 less than −2   **(d)** 8 less than 3
    (e) 2 less than −6   **(f)** 5 more than 2
    (g) 5 more than −1   **(h)** 7 more than −5
    (i) 8 more than −6   **(j)** 3 less than −4
    (k) 4 more than −7   **(l)** 2 more than −10.

10.3 Ordering positive and negative numbers

You can also use a horizontal number line to put positive and negative numbers in order.

Example 4

Write down these numbers in order of size, starting with the smallest:

3, 0, −5, −9, −2, 2, −4, −8.

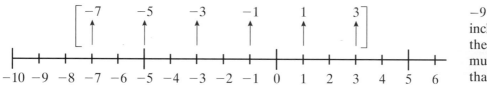

The order is −9, −8, −5, −4, −2, 0, 2, 3.

Example 5

Write down all the odd numbers that are bigger than −9 and smaller than 4.

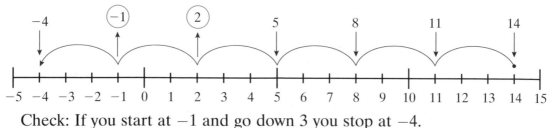

−9 is not included because the numbers must be **bigger** than −9.

Using a horizontal number line the numbers are

−7, −5, −3, −1, 1 and 3.

Sometimes you need to continue a pattern of numbers.

Example 6

Work out the two missing numbers in each number pattern:

(a) 14, 11, 8, 5, ____, ____, −4

(b) −9, −7, −5, −3, ____, ____, 3

(a) The numbers go down by 3 each time.
    The missing numbers are 2 and −1.

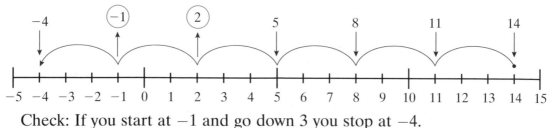

Check: If you start at −1 and go down 3 you stop at −4.

(b) The numbers go up by 2 each time.
The missing numbers are −1 and 1.

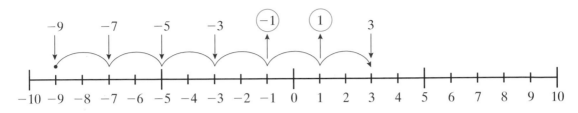

Check: If you start at 1 and go up 2 you reach 3.

Exercise 10C

Use a number line to help you with these questions.

1 Write down these numbers in order of size, starting with the smallest:
   (a) 4, −8, −2, −5, 7, −4   **(b)** 5, −4, 2, −5, 1, −10
   (c) −6, 6, −9, 1, −3, −2   **(d)** −3, 5, 8, −10, 2, −5
   (e) 3, −9, 2, 1, −8, −4   **(f)** 9, 2, −8, −2, −6, −5
   (g) −9, 2, −7, 4, −8, −1   **(h)** −11, 5, 12, −6, −3, −9

2 Write down the next two numbers in each pattern:
   (a) 7, 5, 3, 1, . . .   **(b)** 8, 5, 2, −1, . . .
   (c) 15, 11, 7, 3, . . .   **(d)** 10, 6, 2, −2, . . .
   (e) 2, 0, −2, −4, . . .   **(f)** 12, 8, 4, 0, . . .
   (g) 5, 1, −3, −7, . . .   **(h)** −9, −7, −5, −3, . . .

3 Write down the next two numbers in each pattern:
   (a) −10, −8, −6, −4, . . .   **(b)** −11, −8, −5, −2, . . .
   (c) −8, −5, −2, 1, . . .   **(d)** −7, −5, −3, −1, . . .
   (e) −13, −9, −5, −1, . . .   **(f)** −10, −7, −4, −1, . . .
   (g) −10, −9, −7, −4, . . .   **(h)** −11, −9, −5, 1, . . .

4 Work out the two missing numbers in each pattern:
   (a) 11, 8, 5, 2, _____, _____, −7.
   (b) −10, −7, −4, −1, _____, _____, 8
   (c) 17, 13, 9, 5, _____, _____, −7
   (d) −14, −9, −4, 1, _____, _____, 16
   (e) 4, 1, −2, −5, _____, _____, −14
   (f) 11, 10, 8, 5, _____, _____, −10

5 Write down all the numbers that are larger than −5 and smaller than 3.

6 Write down all the odd numbers that are larger than −8 and smaller than 3.

7 Write down all the even numbers that are smaller than 6 and larger than −7.

8 Write down all the multiples of 3 that are smaller than 9 and larger than −7.

10.4 Adding and subtracting positive and negative numbers

When you add or subtract numbers, the positive and negative signs make a difference:

Adding a positive number
Adding a negative number

Subtracting a positive number
Subtracting a negative number

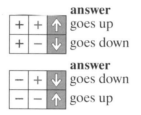

Adding ice makes a drink colder:

What if you take ice away?

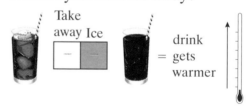

Example 7

Use the table above to find the answers.

1   **(a)** +2 + +5   **(b)** +9 + −4
    (c) +10 − +4   **(d)** +5 − −4

  (a) + 2 + + 5 = + 7   **(b)** + 9 + − 4 = + 5

        answer goes up   answer goes down

  (c) − 10 − + 4 = − 14   **(d)** + 5 − − 4 = + 9

        answer goes down   answer goes up

Exercise 10D

1 Use this table to help you answer these questions:

(a) $+3 - 2 = 1$ (b) $+3 - -2$
(c) $+2 - +3$ (d) $-1 - +2$
(e) $0 - +2$ (f) $-2 - -2$
(g) $+2 - 0$ (h) $-1 - -1$

First Number

$-$	$+3$	$+2$	$+1$	0	-1	-2	-3
$+3$	0	-1	-2	-3	-4	-5	-6
$+2$	1	0	-1	-2	-3	-4	-5
$+1$	2	1	0	-1	-2	-3	-4
0	3	2	1	0	-1	-2	-3
-1	4	3	2	1	0	-1	-2
-2	5	4	3	2	1	0	-1
-3	6	5	4	3	2	1	0

Second Number

$+3 - +2 = 1$

Use the rules shown to answer these questions.

2 (a) $+5 + +3$ (b) $-3 + +5$
   (c) $+2 + +4$ (d) $-5 + +3$
   (e) $4 + +2$ (f) $-12 + +1$
   (g) $-5 + +4$ (h) $-1 + +2$

answer

| $+$ | $+$ | ↑ | goes up |
| $+$ | $-$ | ↓ | goes down |

answer

| $-$ | $+$ | ↓ | goes down |
| $-$ | $-$ | ↑ | goes up |

3 (a) $+4 + -3$ (b) $+2 + -5$
   (c) $-5 + -1$ (d) $+3 + -2$
   (e) $-8 + -2$ (f) $-2 + -3$
   (g) $-7 + -5$ (h) $-1 + -3$

4 (a) $+4 - +2$ (b) $+5 - +3$ (c) $+2 - +9$
   (d) $+1 - +4$ (e) $-3 - +4$ (f) $-2 - +5$
   (g) $-4 - +2$ (h) $-8 - +3$ (i) $-1 - +6$

5 (a) $+6 - -2$ (b) $+3 - -9$ (c) $+5 - -3$
   (d) $+8 - -3$ (e) $-3 - -5$ (f) $-5 - -2$
   (g) $-4 - -1$ (h) $-2 - -4$ (i) $-7 - -1$

6 (a) $-4 + +5$ (b) $-9 - +4$ (c) $-3 - -2$
   (d) $+8 + -3$ (e) $-2 + -8$ (f) $-5 + +1$
   (g) $+9 - +2$ (h) $+8 - -4$ (i) $-6 + +6$

7   **(a)** $-2 + +4 - +3$ **(b)** $-5 + -3 - -4$ **(c)** $+2 - -7 + -5$

　 (d) $-4 - +3 + -5$ **(e)** $+9 + -2 - -6$ **(f)** $-5 + -8 - +6$

Summary of key points

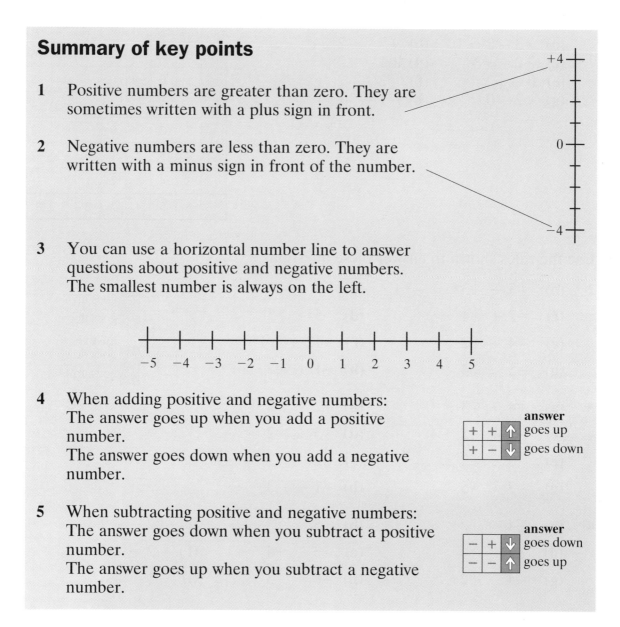

1   Positive numbers are greater than zero. They are sometimes written with a plus sign in front.

2   Negative numbers are less than zero. They are written with a minus sign in front of the number.

3   You can use a horizontal number line to answer questions about positive and negative numbers. The smallest number is always on the left.

4   When adding positive and negative numbers:
The answer goes up when you add a positive number.
The answer goes down when you add a negative number.

			answer
+	+	⬆	goes up
+	−	⬇	goes down

5   When subtracting positive and negative numbers:
The answer goes down when you subtract a positive number.
The answer goes up when you subtract a negative number.

			answer
−	+	⬇	goes down
−	−	⬆	goes up

11 Graphs

11.1 Coordinate grids

This coordinate grid shows the map of an island. The lookout tower is positioned at the centre of the grid. Its coordinates are (0, 0). The point (0, 0) is called the origin.

Remember:
Always go across first

⟷

then go up or down

↕

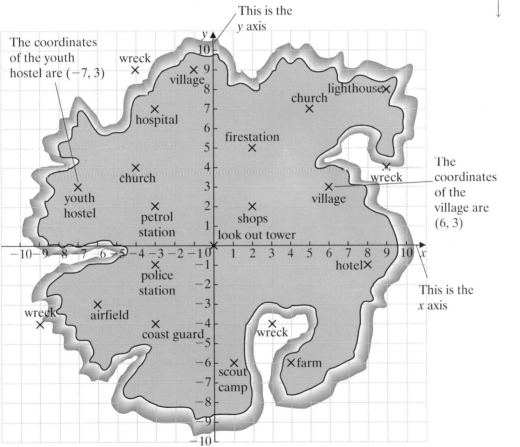

The coordinates of the youth hostel are (−7, 3)

This is the y axis

The coordinates of the village are (6, 3)

This is the x axis

Hint:
x is across

■ **The horizontal coordinate is called the *x*-coordinate.**

■ **The vertical coordinate is called the *y*-coordinate. You always write the *x*-coordinate first.**

Remember:
x comes before y in the alphabet

Exercise 11A

1 What are the co-ordinates of:
   (a) airfield   **(b)** fire station
   (c) church (2 answers)   **(d)** lighthouse
   (e) village (2 answers)   **(f)** wreck (4 answers)
   (g) coast guard

2 What can be found at:
   (a) $(-3, 7)$ **(b)** $(8, -1)$ **(c)** $(2, 2)$ **(d)** $(1, -6)$
   (e) $(4, -6)$ **(f)** $(-3, -1)$ **(g)** $(-3, 2)$

3 This grid shows the layout of an exhibition hall.
   (a) What are the coordinates of:
      (i) fire exits (4 answers)
      (ii) entrance posts (2)
      (iii) security posts (2)
      (iv) cloakrooms (2)
   (b) What can be found at:
      (i) $(0, 5)$ **(ii)** $(-4, 1)$
      (iii) $(5, 1)$ **(iv)** $(-5, 4)$
      (v) $(0, -2)$ **(vi)** $(0, 0)$

Key to grid:
FE – fire exit   E – entrance
SP – security   C – cloakroom
PA – children's play area   FF – food sale
TO – ticket office   LF – lost and found
AB – advance booking

4 Complete each shape on the grid and write down the coordinates of each corner.

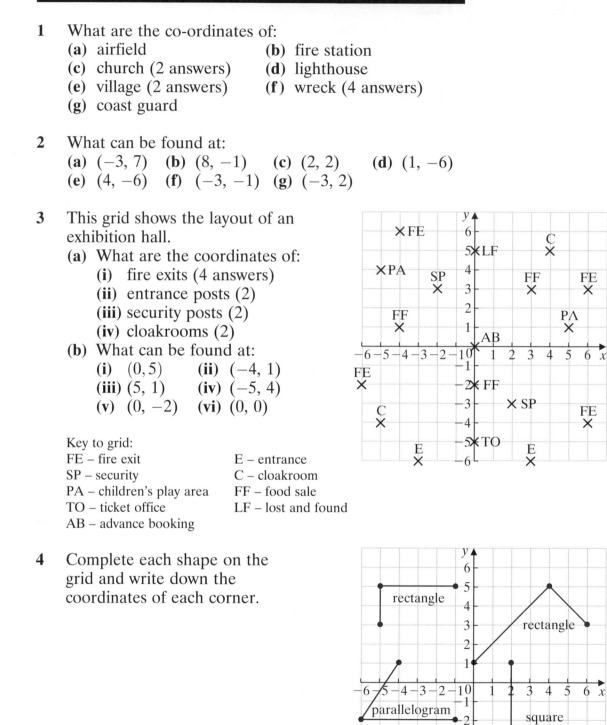

5 Draw a coordinate grid from −8 to 8 on both axes.
  (a) Plot the following points and join them in order:
      (7, 8) → (−6, 8) → (−6, −6) → (5, −6) → (5, 6)
      → (−4, 6) → (−4, −4) → (3, −4) →
  (b) Write down any pattern that you see.
  (c) Plot the next 5 points and write down their
      coordinates.

6 This grid shows part of the coastline:

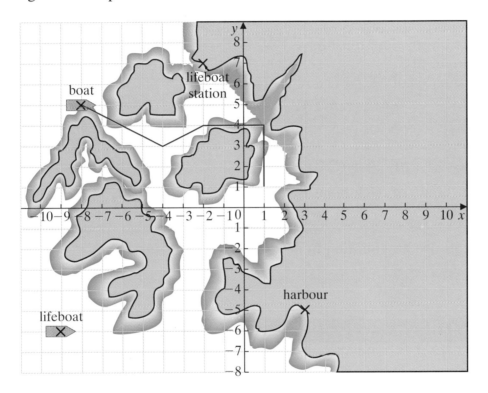

  (a) To get to the harbour the boat's route starts:
      (−8, 5) to (−4, 3) to (−2, 4) to (1, 4) to (1, 1) …
      List the remaining moves for the boat to get to the
      harbour.
  (b) List the coordinate moves for the lifeboat to get
      back to the lifeboat station.

11.2 Equations of lines

You can describe straight lines on a graph with an
equation. The equation of a line tells you what points can
be on the line.

The coordinate grid shows people in a marching band at the start of their routine. A, B, C and D are standing in a straight line. Their coordinates are:

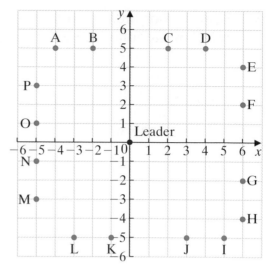

$$A \rightarrow (-4, 5)$$
$$B \rightarrow (-2, 5)$$
$$C \rightarrow (2, 5)$$
$$D \rightarrow (4, 5)$$

The y-coordinate of each point is 5.
The equation of the line is $y = 5$.
Any points on this line must have a y-coordinate of 5.
The co-ordinates of M, N, O and P are:

$$M \rightarrow (-5, -3)$$
$$N \rightarrow (-5, -1)$$
$$O \rightarrow (-5, 1)$$
$$P \rightarrow (-5, 3)$$

The x-coordinate of each point is -5 so the equation of the line is $x = -5$.

■ **You can use an equation to describe a straight line.**
For example: $x = -5$

Exercise 11B

1   In the diagram above what is the equation of the line joining:
    (a) E, F, G and H
    (b) I, J, K and L?

2   Half way through the display the band is in the position shown on the grid.
    What are the equations of the lines joining the points:

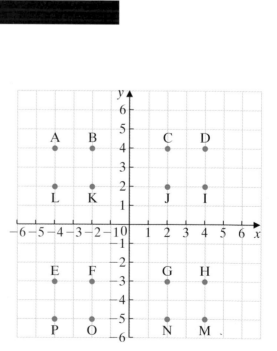

(a) ABCD	(b) ALEP
(c) DIHM	(d) LKJI
(e) EFGH	(f) BKFO?

(Hint: write the coordinates of each point first.)

3 Look at the grid.
What would you call the
line joining the points:

(a) ABCD
(b) AML
(c) BPNK
(d) LJIGF
(e) CRSH
(f) PQR
(g) DEF
(h) MNE?

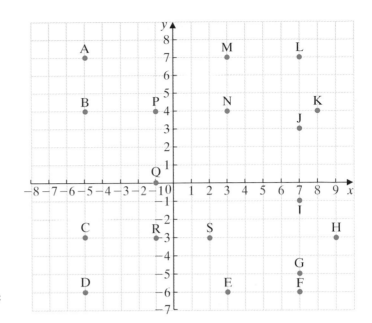

4 What is the equation of the
line joining these points:

(a) $(1, 2)$ $(1, 3)$ $(1, 5)$
(c) $(-2, 2)$ $(2, 2)$ $(3, 2)$
(e) $(2, -4)$ $(4, -4)$ $(6, -4)$

(b) $(-1, -3)$ $(2, -3)$ $(4, -3)$
(d) $(0, -1)$ $(0, 2)$ $(0, 6)$
(f) $(-6, -3)$ $(-6, -1)$ $(-6, 2)$

11.3 Drawing lines from equations

You can draw any straight line if you know the position of
two or more points on it.

Example 1

Draw the line with equation $x = 5$.

First, work out the two points
that will be on the line …

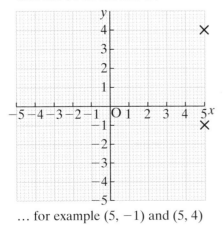

… for example $(5, -1)$ and $(5, 4)$

Join the points together
and label the line:

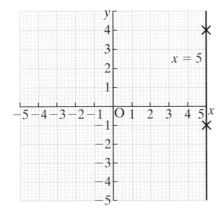

1 Draw the line for each equation on a copy of this −6 to 6 grid.

    (a) $x = 4$ **(b)** $y = -2$
    (c) $x = -3$ **(d)** $y = 5$
    (e) $x = 1$ **(f)** $y = -5$

2 Draw a −6 to 6 coordinate grid and draw each set of lines on it. Name the shape produced each time.

    (a) $x = 5, x = 1, y = 3, y = -1$
    (b) $x = -6, x = -3, y = 5, y = -4$
    (c) $x = -2, x = 2, y = 5, y = -2$

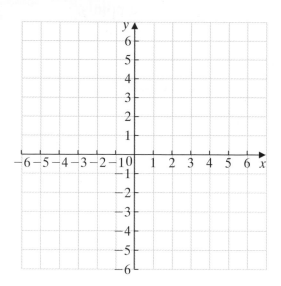

11.4 Equations of sloping lines

When a line on a graph is sloping, you can find its equation by finding the rule that links the coordinates of the points.
The points A, B, C, D and E on the diagram make a straight line.
Look at the coordinates of the points A, B, C, D and E:

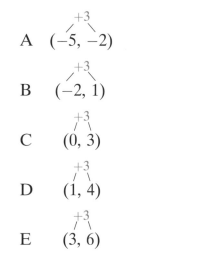

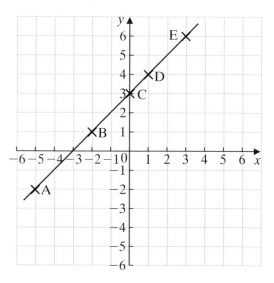

The rule to find the y-coordinate is 'add 3 to the x-coordinate'.
The equation of the line is $y = x + 3$

Exercise 11D

1   Find the equation of each
    line on the diagram:

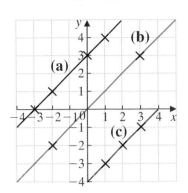

2   Find the equation
    of these lines:

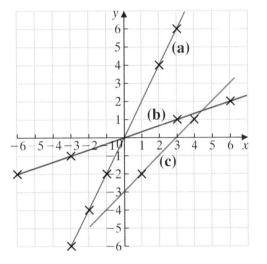

11.5 Drawing sloping lines using tables

Drawing sloping lines is easy using a table.

Example 2

Draw the graph of $y = x + 4$.

- Choose values of x
  e.g. $-3, -2, -1, 0, 1, 2, 3$.
- Draw a table:

x	-3	-2	-1	0	1	2	3
y							

● Work out y for each value of x:

e.g. $x = -3$ $y = -3 + 4 = 1$ $y = 1$
     $x = -2$ $y = -2 + 4 = 2$ $y = 2$

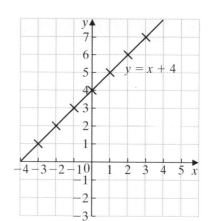

x	-3	-2	-1	0	1	2	3
y	1	2	3	4	5	6	7

● Plot the coordinate pairs on your grid:
(-3, 1) (-2, 2) (-1, 3) (0, 4) (1, 5) (2, 6) (3, 7)

● Draw in and label the line.

Example 3

Draw the graph of $y = 2x + 3$.

● Choose values of x: -3, -2, -1, 0, 1, 2, 3
● Draw a table

x	-3	-2	-1	0	1	2	3
y							

● Work out y for each value of x:

e.g. $x = 0$ $y = (2 \times 0) + 3 = 3$ $y = 3$
     $x = 1$ $y = (2 \times 1) + 3 = 5$ $y = 5$

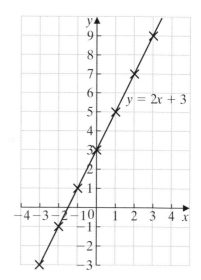

x	-3	-2	-1	0	1	2	3
y	-3	-1	1	3	5	7	9

● Plot the coordinate pairs on your grid
(-3, -3) (-2, -1) (-1, 1) (0, 3) (1, 5)
(2, 7) (3, 9)

● Draw in and label the line.

Exercise 11E

1 For each equation:

● Copy and complete the table of values.
● Plot the points on a coordinate grid and draw the line.

(a) $y = x + 2$

−3	−2	−1	0	1	2	3
		1				5

(b) $y = x - 1$

−3	−2	−1	0	1	2	3
	−3			0		

(c) $y = 2x + 1$

−3	−2	−1	0	1	2	3
	−3				5	

(d) $y = 3x - 1$

−3	−2	−1	0	1	2	3
	−7				5	

(e) $y = 3x + 2$

−3	−2	−1	0	1	2	3
	−4					11

(f) $y = 5x + 1$

−3	−2	−1	0	1	2	3
	−9					

(g) $y = 3 - 2x$

−3	−2	−1	0	1	2	3
9	7					

(h) $y = 1 - x$

−3	−2	−1	0	1	2	3
9	7					

11.6 Conversion graphs

Conversion graphs show relationships between different units.
This graph shows the relationship between millimetres and
inches.

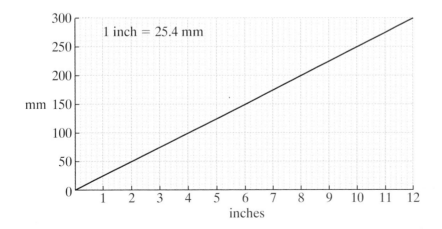

You can use a graph like this to convert from one to the
other.

Example 4

Use the graph to convert:
(a) 4 inches to millimetres   **(b)** 125 millimetres to inches.

(a)

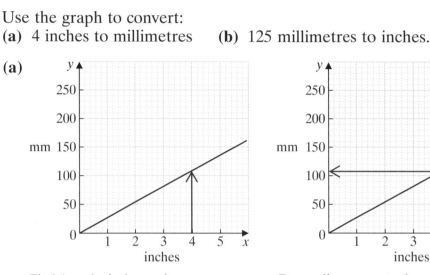

Find 4 on the inches scale.
Draw a vertical line up to the graph.

Draw a line across to the mm scale and
read off the answer:
4 inches is just over 100 mm.

(b)

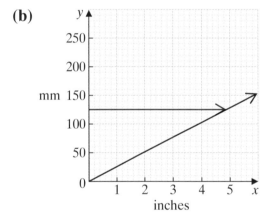
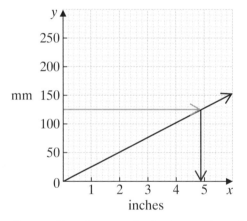

Find 125 on the mm scale.
Draw a line up across to the graph.

Draw a line down to the inches scale and
read off the answer:
125 mm is just under 5 inches.

■ **A conversion graph shows a relationship on a coordinate grid.**

11.7 Using a scale

Conversion graphs will often use different scales on each axis.

The most common scales to use are the factors of 10: 1, 2, 5, 10 and multiples of 10: 10, 20, 50, 100.

You work out a scale like this:

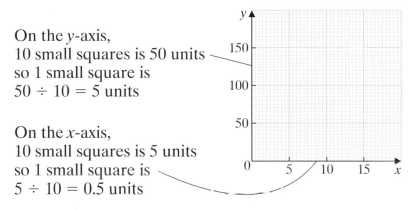

On the *y*-axis,
10 small squares is 50 units
so 1 small square is
50 ÷ 10 = 5 units

On the *x*-axis,
10 small squares is 5 units
so 1 small square is
5 ÷ 10 = 0.5 units

Always remember to count in the scale that you are using.

For example, if you use 10 small squares for 5 units, count in 5s: 5, 10, 15, . . .

If you use 10 small squares for 50 units, count in 50s: 50, 100, 150, 200, . . .

Exercise 11F

1   This conversion graph shows the relationship between the lengths of a pipe and its weight.
    (a) Work out the scale on each axis.
    (b) Use the graph to find:
        (i) the weight of a 20 metre pipe.
        (ii) the weight of a 5 metre pipe
        (iii) the length of a pipe weighing 80 kg.

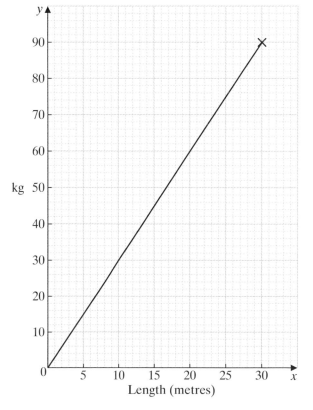

2   The graph shows the relationship between the length
    of side of a square and its perimeter.
    (a) Work out the scale on each axis.
    (b) Use the graph to find:
       (i)   the perimeter of a square with side 30 cm
       (ii) the perimeter of a square with side 18 cm
       (iii) the length of side if the perimeter is 140 cm
       (iv) the length of side if the perimeter is 108 cm.

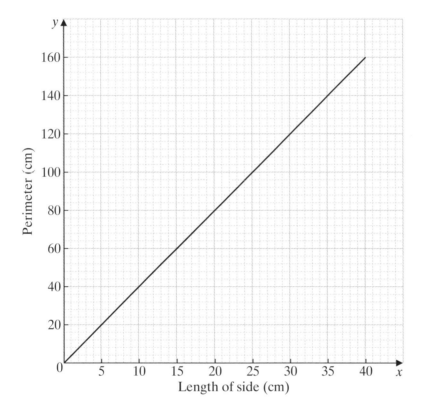

3   Draw a coordinate grid on some graph paper.
    Label the *x*-axis: Weight of metal (kg) and the
    y-axis: Time to melt (minutes)
    Use a scale of 5 small squares = 5 kg on *x*-axis.
    and 5 small squares = 1 minute on the *y*-axis.
    Plot the points (0, 0) and (40, 10) and join them up.
    This graph tells you how long it takes to melt
    different weights of metal.
    Use the graph to find out:
    (a) how long it takes to melt 10 kg
    (b) how long it takes to melt 32 kg
    (c) how much metal you can melt in 7 minutes
    (d) how much metal melts in 4 minutes.

Remember to count
in your scale.

It takes 0 minutes to
melt 0 kg and
10 minutes to melt
40 kg of the metal.
So you can plot
(0, 0) and (40, 10).
Join the two points
to complete the
conversion graph.

4 £10 sterling = 80 francs
Use this information to plot a conversion graph
between pounds and francs.

Use the graph to find:
(a) how many pounds are there in 60 francs.
(b) how many francs are there in £15.
(c) how many francs = £1.

Hint:
£0 = 0 francs so
you can plot the
point (0, 0).

5 It is recommended that a 10-year-old child needs
11 hours of sleep a day and a 2-year-old needs 15 hours.
Use these two pieces of information to produce a
conversion graph to compare age of child to hours of
sleep needed.

Use your graph to find out:
(a) how much sleep a 7-year-old needs
(b) how much sleep a 1-year-old needs (extend your line)
(c) what age child needs 8 hours sleep (extend your line)
(d) how old a child is who needs $14\frac{1}{2}$ hours sleep.

Plot (2, 15) and
(10, 11) join the
points with a
straight line.
Think carefully
about scales.

Conversion graphs can be used for all four quadrants:

Example 5

The graph shows how to convert between °Celsius and °Fahrenheit.

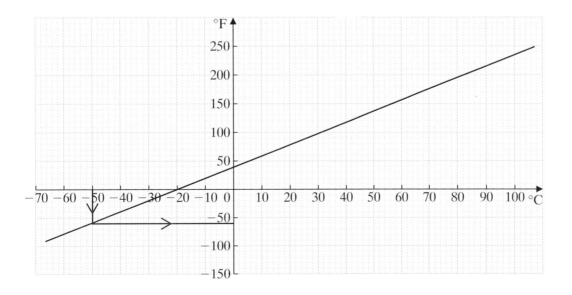

Use the graph to find the temperature in °F equal to −50 °C.

● Find −50 °C on the °C axis.
● Draw down to the graph.
● Draw across to the °F axis.
● Read off the value.

−50°C = −60°F

So −50°C is −60°F

Exercise 11G

1 Use the conversion graph above to convert:
(a) 40 °C to °F
(b) 200 °F to °C
(c) −100 °F to °C
(d) −60 °C to °F
(e) 0 °F to °C

Summary of key points

1 The horizontal coordinate is called the *x*-coordinate. The vertical coordinate is called the *y*-coordinate. You always write the *x*-coordinate first.

2 You can use an equation to describe a straight line. For example: $x = -5$

3 A conversion graph shows a relationship on a coordinate grid.

12 Handling data

12.1 Sources of data

Information, often called **data**, comes from all different kinds of sources. Here are some of them:

Information is often given in tables. This exercise will give you practice in using tables.

Exercise 12A

1 This extract from a database gives the marks some pupils in 8B got in the end of term exam.

Name	English	Maths	History	Geography	Science	German
Barbara	38	43	46	64	48	56
Brian	45	50	48	56	55	47
Chawla	34	46	52	60	52	39
Denzil	43	55	63	57	61	42
Fenella	63	70	65	52	68	53
Judith	39	44	58	69	51	49
Kenneth	76	72	61	57	77	44

(a) How many marks did Denzil get in Science?
(b) Who scored 69 in Geography?
(c) Which pupil scored 52 in two subjects?
(d) How many marks were there over 65?
(e) How many marks did Kenneth get altogether?
(f) Who had the highest marks in
  (i) Geography   (ii) History?

2   **SUPERDEAL HOLIDAYS to LAKE GARDA**

Date	Board	7 nights	10 nights	11 nights	14 nights
Sat: May 16, 23, 30	B&B	£199	—	£269	£309
	Half-board	£269	—	£379	£449
Wed: May 20, 27, June 3	B&B	£179	£239	11 nights for the price of 10	£289
	Half-board	£249	£339		£429

(a) How much will it cost for 7 nights bed and breakfast leaving on May 27th?

(b) How much will it cost for 14 nights half-board leaving on May 23rd?

(c) Mr and Mrs Goodtime book 11 nights leaving on May 30th.
   (i) What will the cost be for bed and breakfast?
   (ii) How much extra will it be if they have half-board?

(d) Andy Bakewell decides to leave on June 3rd. How much will it cost him for half-board for 11 nights?

(e) What choice is there if a holidaymaker decides to pay £269?

12.2 Discrete data

■ **Data which you can count is called discrete data.**
For example, the number of children in a family.

■ **You can display discrete data in a bar chart or a pictogram.**

Example 1

Caroline and Hamid counted the number of pupils in their classes who were late for school. Their results were:

Caroline

Day	Tally	Frequency
Mon	⊮ |||	8
Tue	⊮		6
Wed	⊮ ⊮	10
Thur	⊮	5
Fri	⊮		6

Hamid

Day	Tally	Frequency
Mon	⊮		6
Tue	⊮ ||||	9
Wed	⊮ |||	8
Thur	⊮ ||	7
Fri	||||	4

Remember:
This table is called a tally chart or a frequency table.

(a) Show Caroline's results in a bar chart.
(b) Show Hamid's results in a pictogram.
(c) Compare the two sets of data in a dual bar chart.

(a)

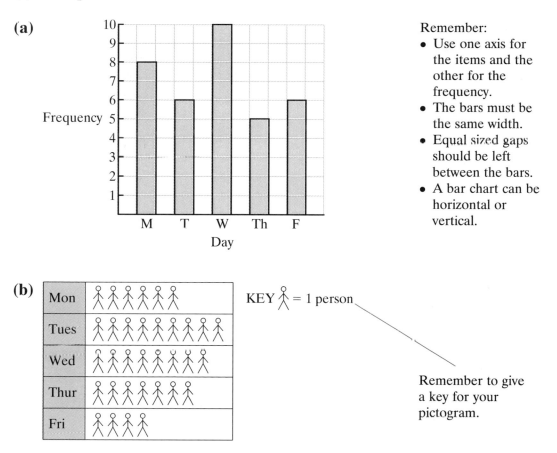

Remember:
- Use one axis for the items and the other for the frequency.
- The bars must be the same width.
- Equal sized gaps should be left between the bars.
- A bar chart can be horizontal or vertical.

(b)

Mon	𝘈𝘈𝘈𝘈𝘈𝘈
Tues	𝘈𝘈𝘈𝘈𝘈𝘈𝘈𝘈𝘈
Wed	𝘈𝘈𝘈𝘈𝘈𝘈𝘈𝘈
Thur	𝘈𝘈𝘈𝘈𝘈𝘈𝘈
Fri	𝘈𝘈𝘈𝘈

KEY 𝘈 = 1 person

Remember to give a key for your pictogram.

(c) A dual bar chart is used to compare two sets of data. You just put the bars for each set of data next to each other.

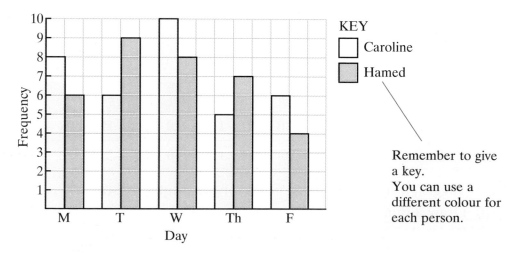

KEY
☐ Caroline
▨ Hamed

Remember to give a key.
You can use a different colour for each person.

Exercise 12B

1   The number of pairs of shoes sold by a shoe shop in one week is given in the table.

Size of shoe	3	4	5	6	7	8	9	10
No. sold	4	8	16	20	22	20	12	7

Represent this on a bar chart.

2   The number of pairs of shoes sold in one week by a larger store is given in the table.

Size of shoe	3	4	5	6	7	8	9	10
No. sold	64	70	84	76	80	96	66	54

Represent this on a bar chart.

Hint: To fit this data on a bar chart, start the vertical axis at 50:

This reminds you that part of the scale is missing

3   A smallholding in Kent has the following trees:

Type	Apple (Cox)	Apple (Russet)	Apple (Bath)	Pear	Plum (Victoria)	Plum (Golden)	Cherry
Number	84	72	64	78	86	70	76

Draw a bar chart, starting your frequency scale at 50, to illustrate this data.

4   A country garden is laid out as in the table

Type	Lawn	Paths/Patio	Flowers	Pond	Orchard	Vegetables
m²	156	110	96	120	104	88

Draw a bar chart to illustrate this data.

5   The number of ferries leaving port is given in the table.

Month	Jan	Feb	Mar	Apr	May	Jun	Jul	Aug	Sep	Oct	Nov	Dec
Quickline	82	94	106	110	102	116	128	130	118	98	86	80
Speedcraft	74	78	88	96	110	124	140	120	92	82	74	72

(a) Suggest a suitable starting point for the frequency scale.

(b) Draw a dual bar graph to represent this data.

(c) Write three sentences to comment on your graphs.

6   The table shows the number of days pupils were absent from school last week.

```
3 1 0 2 0 5 4 0 5 2
0 2 1 0 4 0 1 5 2 5
2 0 0 3 1 5 2 0 1 4
5 1 0 2 1 0 0 3 0 5
0 2 1 0 5 0 4 1 2 0
```

(a) Draw a frequency table to represent this data.

(b) Represent this using:
    (i) a pictogram   (ii) a bar graph.

(c) Which do you think is the most useful? Give your reason.

7   Amina rolled two dice 60 times and added up the total each time. Her results were:

```
8   5   7  10   5  7   9   3  11   8
6  12   6   4   8  6   7  10   5   7
7   8   2  11   7  9   6   8   6  10
11   3   6   5   8  4   7   2   9   6
9   7  10   7  11  6  12   5   7   8
7   8   4   9   7  7   8   3  10   5
```

(a) Draw up a frequency table.

(b) Draw a bar chart to represent this data.

(c) Comment on your result.

(d) Try the experiment yourself and compare your results to Amina's

8   The numbers of saloon and estate cars sold by Rutland Garage in the first six weeks of 1999 were:

Week	1	2	3	4	5	6
Saloon	5	4	6	7	12	9
Estate	3	6	8	2	7	5

(a) Draw a dual bar graph to represent this data.

(b) Comment on your result.

9 Harold conducted a survey about meals. He noted down what people had as their main course:

Meat, meat, poultry, sausage, omelette, pizza, quorn, fish, meat, fish, poultry, pizza, fish, meat, fish, poultry, omelette, pizza, meat, fish, sausage, fish, meat, fish, poultry, quorn, meat, omelette, sausage, pizza, fish, quorn, meat, poultry, poultry, meat, poultry, fish, pizza, meat, fish, poultry, omelette, meat, fish, pizza, fish, meat, sausage, fish.

Represent this data by drawing:
- a frequency table.
- a bar chart.
- a bar-line graph.

> A bar-line graph is the same as a bar chart but you don't draw the whole bar, just a line.

10 Positions in a series of tests were:

Name	English	Maths	Craft	Games	Geography	Science
Angela	3rd	4th	6th	5th	2nd	3rd
Peter	5th	1st	4th	2nd	7th	4th

(a) Draw a dual bar graph to represent this data.

(b) Comment on your result.

12.3 Grouping data

When data is widely spread out it is better to group the data so you can spot any patterns.

For example, the marks out of 60 for a test are shown in the table:

```
30  27  33  12  42  24  37  56  31  38
22  51   9  28  50  19  33  21   8  57
17  48  47  37  25  35  48  15  26  43
38  11  32  55  33  45  40  38  52  34
56  21  48  40  28  50  24  40  19  46
23  38  15  25  40   5  35  51  28  56
```

If you plot the data as it is given, a bar-line graph would look like this:

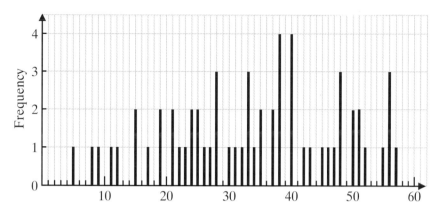

This doesn't give much information as the data is so spread out.

Instead, you group the data like this:

Mark	Tally	Frequency
1–10	|||	3
11–20	⊞ ||	7
21–30	⊞ ⊞ ||||	14
31–40	⊞ ⊞ ⊞ |||	18
41–50	⊞ ⊞	10
51–60	⊞ |||	8

Hint:
The groups should be the same size.
The groups are called **class intervals**.

Then the graph looks like this:

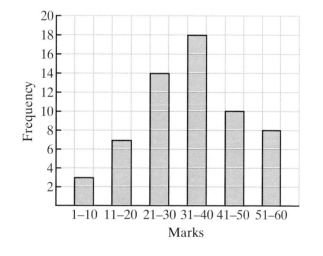

Exercise 12C

1   In September the number of boxes of fruit and
    vegetables a shopkeeper buys each day is:

    25 31   8 38 19 31
    42 26 17 22 40 26
    16 35 21 15 37 43
    30 20 34   9 29 14
    28 45 12 23 39 21

    (a) Using class intervals of 0–4, 5–9, 10–14, and so on,
        represent this on a bar graph.
    (b) Which class interval represents the most frequent
        purchase?

2   The table shows the number of soft drinks sold at
    breaktime over a one month period.

    11 26   3 37 28 20 25 12 22 29 16 24 26 15 23
    24 16 33 12 17 28 15 26 32 19 22   0 12 21 29
    34   6 17 20 28 18   4 22   7 20 13 23 32 16 11
    16 24 18   9 10 22 28 14 27 18 23 26 16   5 21

    (a) Using class intervals 0–4, 5–9, 10–14, 15–19, . . .
        35–39, draw up a frequency table.
    (b) Draw a bar chart.
    (c) Using class intervals 0–9, 10–19, 20–29, 30–39,
        draw up another frequency table.
    (d) Draw a bar chart representing this data.
    (e) Which chart do you think is the most useful? Give
        your reason.

3   When training for a distance cycle race the number of
    kilometres Brian rode each day was:

    21 44 15 54 20 46 23 55 40 45
    38 55 36 24 45 52 35 43 56 36
    60 26 45 18 32 48 50 58 30 58
    44 15 38 52 48 27 34 42 60 45

    (a) Using class intervals of 1–10, 11–20, 21–30, etc.,
        represent this on a bar chart.
    (b) Comment on your result.

4 The numbers of faulty items produced by two types of machines were, per thousand:

No. of faulty items	0–3	4–7	8–11	12–15	16–19	Over 20
Machine A	22	18	12	14	7	3
Machine B	14	12	10	8	5	6

(a) Draw a dual bar graph to represent this data.
(b) Comment on the results.

5 Year 8 were given a spelling test in January and repeated it in March. The marks for 40 pupils were:

January

16	23	26	35	42
24	42	15	23	30
12	8	12	31	16
33	26	34	41	38
36	13	5	31	29
44	24	32	12	35
27	17	45	23	30
34	41	27	26	42

March

45	25	30	46	28
36	43	25	27	33
21	20	16	36	46
32	44	31	42	39
15	35	22	35	24
45	26	32	48	36
41	18	27	40	43
28	37	42	28	37

(a) Using class intervals 1–10, 11–20, etc., draw up a frequency table for each test.
(b) Draw a dual bar graph to show the results.
(c) Write three sentences commenting on the results.

12.4 A piece of cake

Another way to display data is using a **pie chart**.

■ **A pie chart uses a circle to display data.**
  Each item has a sector of the circle.

Example 2

Richard recorded the colours of the first 20 cars to pass his school. His results were:

black, red, black, blue, silver, black, silver, red, blue, black, silver, blue, black, black, silver, black, white, black, silver, blue.

Draw a pie chart to illustrate the data.

Step 1: work out the angle for each car.
There are 360° in a circle.
There are 20 cars.
So each car is 360° ÷ 20 = 18°

Step 2: multiply the frequencies by the angle for each car.

Colour	Frequency	Angle
Black	8	8 × 18° = 144°
Red	2	2 × 18° = 36°
Blue	4	4 × 18° = 72°
Silver	5	5 × 18° = 90°
White	1	1 × 18° = 18°

Remember:
Check the total is 360°:
144 + 36 + 72 + 90 + 18
= 360

Step 3: draw a circle. Mark in the radius:

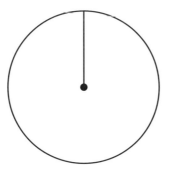

Step 4: measure the angles from the centre in turn:

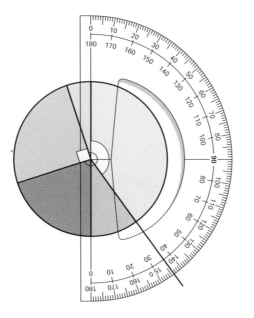

There is more on measuring angles on page 25.

Step 5: label the pie chart.

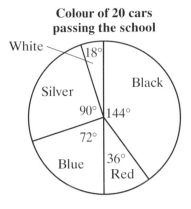

Colour of 20 cars passing the school

White — 18°
Silver
Black
90° 144°
72°
Blue 36°
Red

Exercise 12D

1 The table shows the choice a class of 30 pupils made for a day trip.

Choice	Frequency	Angle on pie chart
Art gallery	8	
Concert	3	
Cinema	4	
Theatre	5	
Museum	10	

(a) What angle would represent one pupil?
(b) Complete the table.
(c) Display this data on a pie chart.

2 Rachel asked 30 pupils 'What is your favourite colour?' The table shows her results:

Colour	Frequency
Green	5
Red	8
Blue	10
Yellow	4
Black	3

Draw a pie chart to illustrate this data.

3 The numbers of papers bought one day by pupils in 8B
were:

Daily Mail The *Sun* The *Express* The *Mirror* The *Telegraph*
  3   6   4   10   1

Draw a pie chart to illustrate this data.

4 In a survey 60 people were asked the question, 'Which
form of transport do you think needs to improve the
most? The replies were:

Train Bus Underground Road Air
 14   24   12   8   2

Draw a pie chart to represent this data.

12.5 Reading a pie chart

To read a pie chart you need to remember that there are
$360°$ in a circle.

Example 3

The pie chart shows which
soup 12 diners chose.

How many people had each
flavour of soup?

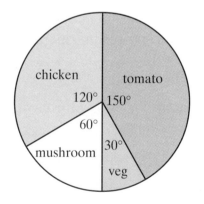

There are 12 people so each person is represented by
$360° \div 12 = 30°$

So: Tomato was chosen by $150° \div 30° = 5$ people
  Vegetable was chosen by $30° \div 30° = 1$ person
  Mushroom was chosen by $60° \div 30° = 2$ people
  Chicken was chosen by $120° \div 30° = 4$ people

Remember:
check that this adds up
to the total:
$5 + 1 + 2 + 4 = 12$

Exercise 12E

1   The pie chart shows the type of ice cream chosen by
    ten students.

    (a) What angle represents one student?
    (b) How many chose each flavour?

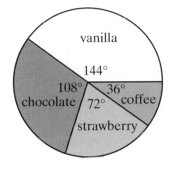

2   The pie chart shows the main hobby of thirty
    students.

    (a) What angle represents one student?
    (b) How many students chose computer
        games?

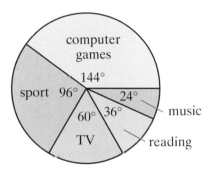

12.6 Are they related?

To work out if two sets of data are related you can draw a
scatter diagram or scatter graph.

■   **A scatter diagram shows the relationship between two**
    sets of data.

Example 4

The table shows the marks of 10 students for Maths and Science.

Maths	56	74	36	48	89	25	30	44	78	63
Science	48	70	36	44	82	16	32	42	71	68

(a) Draw a scatter diagram to illustrate this data.
(b) How are the Maths and Science marks related?

(a) In a scatter diagram you plot one set of data against the other.
The pairs of marks are the coordinates you use.

A mark at (56, 48) means that the student got 56 for maths and 48 for science.

(b) The graph shows an upward trend.
This means that the higher the Maths mark, the higher the Science mark will be.
or the Maths mark increases as the Science mark increases.

This type of trend is called positive **correlation**.

Correlation means how two things are related.

■ **There are three main kinds of correlation.**

Positive correlation

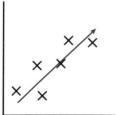

One quantity increases as the other increases.

Negative correlation

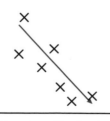

One quantity decreases as the other increases.

No correlation

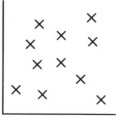

There is no relationship between quantities.

Exercise 12F

1 The numbers of runs scored by two cricket teams were:

Batsman	1	2	3	4	5	6	7	8	9	10	11
Surrey	34	42	106	5	21	32	11	0	9	12	3
Kent	51	6	35	60	44	2	31	18	6	1	8

(a) Draw a scatter diagram.
(b) What correlation is there, if any?

2 The height and the handspan of ten pupils are shown in the table.

Pupil	1	2	3	4	5	6	7	8	9	10
Height (in cm)	156	157	159	160	162	163	165	166	168	170
Handspan (in cm)	20.2	19.5	20.8	20.1	21.8	23.0	24.3	24.1	25.6	27.8

(a) Using a scale from 155 cm to 170 cm on the x-axis, and 19.0 cm to 28.0 cm on the y-axis draw a scatter diagram to show this data.
(b) Comment on the correlation, if any.
(c) Estimate the handspan of a pupil whose height is:
   (i) 158 cm (ii) 169 cm.

3 The table shows the marks of 10 pupils in a series of tests:

Pupil	1	2	3	4	5	6	7	8	9	10
German	40	25	60	30	55	45	35	15	50	20
English	35	65	50	45	30	80	60	30	45	70
Art	25	35	10	30	10	20	25	50	15	20
French	45	20	65	30	60	55	40	15	70	25

(a) Draw scatter diagrams to compare:
   (i) German and French   (ii) German and English
   (iii) German and Art   (iv) French and Art.
(b) Comment on the type of correlation, if any.

12.7 Continuous data

■ **Data that you measure is called continuous data.
For example, temperature, weight, length and time are
all measured.**

■ **Continuous data can be illustrated on a line graph.**

Example 5

The temperature in °C at midday one week in June was:

Day	Mon	Tue	Wed	Thur	Fri	Sat	Sun
Temperature °C	16	18	18	14	17	16	19

Draw a line graph to illustrate this data.

Plot the points then join
them with straight lines:

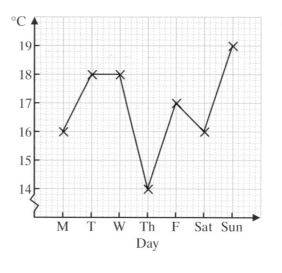

Exercise 12G

1   The average maximum and minimum temperatures,
in °F, in Brighton and Casablanca were:

	Sept	Oct	Nov	Dec	Jan	Feb	Mar	Apr
Brighton	60	55	51	46	42	45	50	56
Casablanca	78	72	68	66	67	70	74	77

(a) On the same axes draw line graphs to show this data.
(b) Make a sensible guess as to what the temperatures
might be in May and June in each place.
(c) Write two things you notice about your graphs.

2 The rainfall, in millimetres, over a six month period was:

Month	Jan	Feb	Mar	Apr	May	Jun
Rainfall (mm)	72	140	82	88	38	24

(a) Draw a line graph to represent this data.
(b) Comment on your graph.
(c) What might the rainfall be in July? Give your reason.

3 The diagrams show part of Sebastian's training schedule.

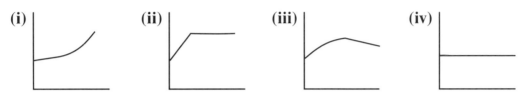

State which diagram fits the following statements:
(a) He speeds up gently and then accelerates.
(b) He increases his pace steadily, reaches a peak and slows down.
(c) He runs at a constant speed.
(d) He increases his pace steadily and then runs at a constant speed.
(e) Draw a diagram which indicates that he 'ran at a constant speed, slowed down, ran at a constant speed again before finishing by sprinting'.

12.8 What's the trend?

■ **Line graphs can also be used to show a trend over a period of time.**

Example 6

The sales figures for a store in thousands of pounds are shown in the table.

Month	Mar	Apr	May	Jun	Jul	Aug	Sept	Oct
Sales (£000)	12	10	14	16	18	17	18	19

(a) Draw a line graph to represent this data.
(b) Describe the trend.
(c) What do you think the figure for November might be? Give a reason.
(d) Suggest a possible reason why there was a slight fall in sales in August.

(a)

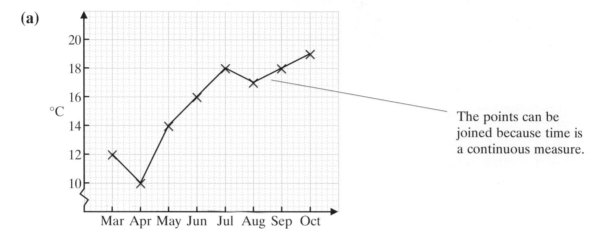

The points can be joined because time is a continuous measure.

(b) The trend is that the sales figures are increasing overall.
(c) £20 000 because the sales are increasing.
(d) People go on holiday in August.

Exercise 12H

1   The value of a car in relation to its age is shown in the table:

Age (years)	0	1	2	3	4	5
Value	£9750	£8000	£7000	£6200	£5400	£4900

(a) Draw a line graph to represent this data.
(b) Comment on your graph.
(c) Use your graph to estimate the value of the car after 6 years.
(d) Estimate the value of the car after 10 years.
(e) Estimate the age of the car when its value is below £2000.

2 An oil painting is valued each year as follows:

1992 £5000	1996 £8000
1993 £5500	1997 £9500
1994 £6100	1998 £11 750
1995 £6900	1999 £13 000

(a) Draw a line graph to show how the value increases.

(b) Estimate the value of the painting in the year 2000.

(c) When might the value of the painting exceed £20 000?

3 The number of births in a village over a six-year period is given in the table.

Year	1992	1993	1994	1995	1996	1997
No. of births	12	17	16	19	20	23

(a) Draw a line graph to represent this data.

(b) Use your graph to estimate the number of births in 1998 and 1999.

4 The table shows the number of cars carried by a ferry company (in hundreds) during the first six months of 1998.

Month	Jan	Feb	Mar	Apr	May	Jun
Number of cars	16	18	21	24	28	35

(a) Draw a line graph to represent this data.

(b) Estimate the number of cars the company might carry in July.

(c) Comment on the trend.

(d) Give one outside factor that might affect the trend over the next six months.

5 The table shows the profit made by a village shopkeeper over the first nine months of 1999.

Month	Jan	Feb	Mar	Apr	May	Jun	Jul	Aug	Sept
Profit	£560	£675	£720	£790	£880	£960	£1120	£1060	£940

(a) Draw a line graph to represent this data.

(b) Comment on the results.

(c) Suggest a likely figure for October. Give your reason.

Summary of key points

1 Data which you can count is called discrete data. For example, the number of children in a family.

2 You can display discrete data in a bar chart or a pictogram.

3 A pie chart uses a circle to display data.
Each item has a sector of the circle.

4 A scatter diagram shows the relationship between two sets of data.

5 There are three main kinds of **correlation**.

Positive correlation   Negative correlation   No correlation

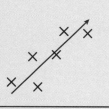 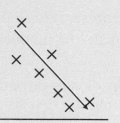 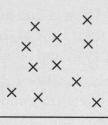

One quantity increases as the other increases.   One quantity decreases as the other increases.   There is no relationship between quantities.

6 Data that you measure is called continuous data.
For example, temperature, weight, length and time are all measured.

7 Continuous data can be illustrated on a line graph.
Line graphs can also be used to show a trend over a period of time.

8 A line graph can be used to:
- illustrate continuous data
- show a trend over a period of time.

13 Formulae and equations

Formulae are used all the time. When you are in a car, your speed is worked out by the formula:

$$\text{speed} = \frac{\text{distance travelled}}{\text{time taken}}$$

30 mph means you travel 30 miles in one hour.

13.1 Word formulae

You can use word formulae to help solve problems.

Remember: formulae is the plural of formula.

Example 1

The formula for the cost of some books is:

cost of books = cost of one book × number bought

John buys 4 books for £5 each. How much does he pay in total?

Use the formula to find out:

$$
\begin{aligned}
\text{cost of books} &= \text{cost of one} \times \text{number bought} \\
&= \quad\quad £5 \quad\quad \times \quad\quad 4 \\
&= £20
\end{aligned}
$$

Example 2

Heather has 3 apples. She buys 4 more.
How many does she have now?
Use the formula:

$$
\begin{aligned}
\text{Total} &= \text{number at start} + \text{number bought} \\
&= \quad\quad 3 \quad\quad + \quad\quad 4 \\
&= 7 \text{ apples}
\end{aligned}
$$

Exercise 13A

1   Amina buys some packets of sweets. She uses the formula:

    cost of sweets = cost of one packet × number bought

    If one packet costs 20p. Find the cost if Amina buys 6 packets.

2   Sam buys some flowers. He uses the formula:

    cost of flowers = cost of one × number bought

    Sam buys 10 flowers at 50p each. Work out the cost of the flowers.

3   Using the formula:

    cost of tapes = cost of one × number bought

    work out the cost of 8 tapes at £7 each.

4   Michael has 20 stamps. He is given 10 more. Write down a word formula for this and use it to work out how many stamps he has altogether.

5   Mark goes shopping and buys a tie costing £7.99. Use a word formula to work out how much change he should receive from a £10 note.

6   Sharon went shopping with a £5 note. She bought a melon costing £1.50. Use a word formula to work out how much change she should get.

7   Write down a word formula to work out the cost of 4 cans of orange drink at 30p each.

8   Keith added together his age and the age of his brother. The total was 28. If Keith's brother was 16 years old, write down a word formula and use it to work out how old Keith was.

9   Simone has 8 conkers. She finds 7 more. Write down and use a word formula to work out how many conkers she has altogether.

10 Narinder bakes 15 cakes. He eats 6 of them straight away. Use a word formula to work out how many cakes are left.

11 Tim and 9 of his friends were playing football and smashed a window. The cost of repairing the window was £110 so the 10 friends decided to split the cost equally between them. Write down a formula for this and use it to work out how much each of them has to pay.

12 Lucy uses this word formula to work out her pay:

pay = hours worked × rate of pay

How much does Lucy get paid for 4 hours at a rate of pay of £3?

13.2 Using letters in formulae

You can use letters in word formulae to stand for unknown amounts.

Example 3

Find a formula for the length of the yellow rod:

length of yellow rod = length of green rod + length of red rod

rewrite using:

y = length of *y*ellow rod
g = length of *g*reen rod
r = length of *r*ed rod

The formula is $y = g + r$

Exercise 13B

1 Write a formula using letters for each of these rod trains.

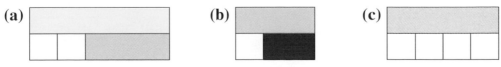

(a)　　　　　　**(b)**　　　　　　**(c)**

2   Write down a formula for the cost C of b bags of sweets at 80 pence for each bag.

3   Sam has f sweets and Tom has g sweets. Write down a formula for the total T sweets.

4   Bianca has r t-shirts and Ricky has s t-shirts. Write down a formula for the total number of t-shirts T.

5   Bhavna has p pens. She gives q of them to Mary. Write down a formula for the number of pens she has left, N.

6   Ali has s sweets. He gives r of them to Ismat. Write down a formula for the number of sweets he has left, N.

7   Write down a formula for the perimeter of this triangle.

Remember: The perimeter is the distance round the outside of a shape.

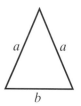

13.3 Formulae with two operations

You need to be able to deal with situations where there will be two operations put together in one formula.

Example 4

Kelly's weekly wages are worked out by:

  weekly wage = hours worked × hourly rate + commission

(a) Write this as a simple formula.
(b) How much will Kelly earn for working 4 hours at £3 per hour with £2 commission?

(a) The formula is:

$$W = hr + c$$

$h \times r$

hours worked   hourly rate

(b) Putting the numbers in the formula:

$$W = 4 \times 3 + 2$$
$$= 12 + 2$$
$$= £14$$

Remember:
You always $\times$
before you $+$

Exercise 13C

Mrs Riley uses this formula to work out how much to pay her staff:

pay = hours worked $\times$ rate of pay + bonus

1   Write this as a formula using letters.

2   Malcolm works for 6 hours one day at a rate of pay of £5 an hour. He earns a bonus of £2. How much does he earn on that day?

3   Natasha works for 30 hours one week at a rate of pay of £4 an hour. She earns a bonus of £5. How much does she earn that week?

4   Vijaya works for 10 hours one week at a rate of pay of £3 an hour. She earns a bonus of £2. How much does she earn that week?

5   Anoushka works for 4 hours one day at a rate of pay of £3.50 an hour. She earns a bonus of £2.50. How much does she earn that day?

Work out the pay of these people using the formula:

$$P = h \times r - d$$

where P stands for pay, h for hours worked, r for rate of pay and d for deductions.

Deductions are taken away from people's pay for Income tax and National Insurance.

6   Bimla works for 10 hours one week at a rate of pay of £5 an hour. She has deductions of £2. How much does she earn that week?

7   Andrew works for 30 hours one week at a rate of pay of £4 an hour. He has deductions of £5. How much does he earn that week?

8   Abbas works for 8 hours one week at a rate of pay of £4 an hour. He has deductions of £2.50. How much does he earn for that week?

9 Naseema works for 12 hours one week at a rate of pay of £2.50 an hour. She has deductions of £1.50. How much does she earn that week?

10 Daphne uses the formula:

number of posts = length of fence in metres ÷ 2 + 1

to work out how many posts she needs to build a fence. How many posts does she need for a fence of length:
(a) 10 metres   **(b)** 20 metres   **(c)** 12 metres?

11 Gareth uses the formula:

$N = t \times 3 + l$

to estimate how far he has travelled along the canal. N stands for the number of miles travelled, t for the number of hours and l for the number of locks. Work out the number of miles he has travelled in:
(a) 4 hours when he has passed through 3 locks
(b) 8 hours when he has passed through 10 locks

12 To work out the cooking time for a lamb joint you use the formula:

cooking time = weight of joint in pounds × 30 minutes + 30 minutes

(a) Write this as a formula using letters.
(b) Find the cooking time for a joint weighing:
   (i) 2 lbs   **(ii)** 1 lb   **(iii)** 7 lbs

13.4 Solving equations

Formulae can be true for many different values but equations are only true for some values:

Equation:	**Formula:**
$x + 4 = 7$	Pay = hours worked × rate of pay $P = h \times r$
This is only true when $x = 3$ The **solution** to this equation is $x = 3$	This works for many different values of h and r.

Finding the value of the letter in an equation is called **solving the equation**.
Sometimes you can solve an equation just by using number facts.

Example 5

Solve the equation:

$a + 3 = 8$

You know that $5 + 3 = 8$ so the solution to this equation is $a = 5$.

Spotting the solution like this is called solving the equation by inspection.

Solve these equations by inspection:

1 $a + 4 = 7$	**2** $b + 4 = 7$	**3** $c + 2 = 5$
4 $d + 3 = 8$	**5** $5 + m = 8$	**6** $6 + n = 13$
7 $2 + p = 3$	**8** $12 + q = 17$	**9** $i - 4 = 0$
10 $j - 5 = 12$	**11** $k - 6 = 16$	**12** $l - 12 = 2$
13 $9 - m = 2$	**14** $32 - n = 12$	**15** $14 - p = 6$
16 $15 - q = 9$	**17** $2 \times r = 10$	**18** $5 \times s = 10$
19 $4 \times t = 12$	**20** $4 \times u = 8$	**21** $3 \times v = 3$
22 $6 \times w = 18$	**23** $3 \times x = 9$	**24** $y \times 2 = 5$
25 $a \div 2 = 4$	**26** $b \div 3 = 2$	**27** $c \div 2 = 5$
28 $d \div 3 = 4$	**29** $20 \div r = 2$	**30** $15 \div s = 3$
31 $16 \div t = 4$	**32** $14 \div u = 7$	**33** $d \div 8 = 4$

You can check your answer by substituting back into the equation:

$a + 4 = 7$

so $\qquad a = 3$

Check:

$3 + 4 = 7$

13.5 Solving equations using number machines

You can't always solve an equation by inspection.
You need to be able to use a systematic method to work out the missing number in equations.

Example 6

Solve the equation:

$a + 4 = 7$

By inspection, the value of a in this equation is 3.
You can write the equation out using a number machine:

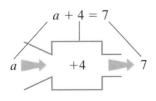

$a + 4 = 7$

$a \rightarrow \boxed{+4} \rightarrow 7$

To solve the equation, use the inverse number machine:

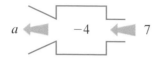

Hint:
−4 is the **inverse**
operation of +4

So $7 - 4 = a$
and $a = 3$

Example 7

Solve the equation $b - 3 = 9$

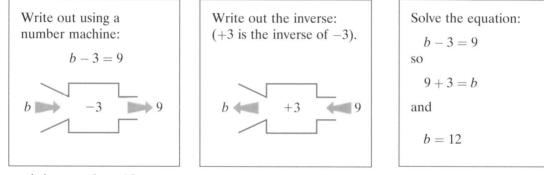

| Write out using a number machine: | Write out the inverse: (+3 is the inverse of −3). | Solve the equation: |

so b is equal to 12.

Exercise 13E

Solve these equations using inverse number machines:

1 $e + 2 = 7$ **2** $f + 2 = 6$ **3** $g + 6 = 10$

4 $h + 5 = 9$ **5** $m + 3 = 7$ **6** $n + 6 = 11$

7 $p + 2 = 3$ **8** $q + 6 = 13$ **9** $a - 4 = 4$

10 $b - 2 = 5$ **11** $c - 1 = 2$ **12** $d - 4 = 5$

13 $m - 3 = 4$ **14** $n - 3 = 2$ **15** $p - 3 = 1$

16 $q - 2 = 5$ **17** $r \times 2 = 40$ **18** $s \times 5 = 35$

19 $t \times 10 = 100$ **20** $v \times 9 = 54$ **21** $12u = 84$

22 $10w = 60$ **23** $2x = 3$ **24** $2y = 3$

25 $a \div 3 = 5$ **26** $b \div 2 = 3$ **27** $c \div 4 = 2$

28 $d \div 3 = 3$ **29** $\dfrac{m}{2} = 2$ **30** $\dfrac{n}{6} = 2$

31 $\dfrac{p}{6} = 2$ **32** $\dfrac{q}{5} = 3$ **33** $\dfrac{18}{n} = 3$

Hint:
$12u$ is the same as
$u \times 12$

Equations with two operations

When you have to solve equations such as
$3p + 2 = 20$ you will need to use two number
machines.

Solve the equation $3p + 2 = 20$.
Write out using number machines:

Work through the machine in reverse
using inverse number machines:

so $(20 - 2) \div 3 = p$
$$18 \div 3 = p$$
$$6 = p$$

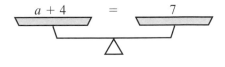

So the solution to $3p + 2 = 20$ is $p = 6$.

Exercise 13F

Solve these equations:

1	$3a + 4 = 13$	**2**	$2b + 7 = 9$

3 $4c + 4 = 12$

4 $5d + 8 = 18$ **5** $2e - 1 = 7$ **6** $3f - 3 = 15$

7 $2g - 4 = 12$ **8** $5h - 1 = 9$ **9** $5i + 1 = 16$

10 $6j + 2 = 26$ **11** $7k + 12 = 26$ **12** $2l + 5 = 23$

13 $3m - 3 = 12$ **14** $2n - 2 = 12$ **15** $5p - 12 = 8$

16 $7q - 14 = 35$ **17** $2r + 8 = 26$ **18** $5s + 3 = 13$

19 $10t + 20 = 90$ **20** $12u + 18 = 30$ **21** $9v - 16 = 20$

22 $10w - 5 = 15$ **23** $2x - 4 = 4$ **24** $2y + 5 = 6$

13.6 Using algebra to solve equations

An equation is a balancing act.

When you solve an equation you must make
sure that both sides balance.

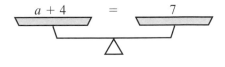

You can solve equations using algebra.

Example 8

Solve $a + 4 = 7$

Think of the equation as a pair of scales:

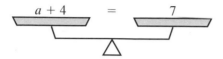

To solve the equation you need to subtract 4 from the left-hand side ...

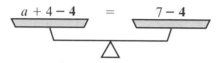

... so you must do the same to the right-hand side to balance the equation.

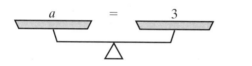

Left-hand side:
$$a + 4 - 4 = a$$

Right-hand side:
$$7 - 4 \quad = 3$$

The scales balance with a on the left and 3 on the right so the solution is $a = 3$.

Example 9

Solve $6c = 18$

Divide both sides by 6:

$$6c \div 6 = c$$
$$18 \div 6 = 3$$

so the solution is $c = 3$.

Exercise 13G

Use algebra to solve these equations:

1 $a + 4 = 8$	**2** $b + 2 = 7$	**3** $c + 3 = 7$
4 $d + 5 = 8$	**5** $e + 2 = 7$	**6** $f + 2 = 6$
7 $g + 6 = 10$	**8** $h + 5 = 9$	**9** $i - 2 = 0$
10 $j - 4 = 10$	**11** $k - 2 = 6$	**12** $l - 3 = 2$

13 $m - 3 = 4$ **14** $n - 3 = 2$ **15** $p - 3 = 1$
16 $q - 2 = 5$ **17** $7e = 21$ **18** $3f = 36$
19 $2g = 24$ **20** $5h = 30$ **21** $5i = 0$
22 $6j = 36$ **23** $8k = 24$ **24** $5l = 20$
25 $a \div 3 = 5$ **26** $b \div 2 = 3$ **27** $c \div 4 = 2$

28 $d \div 3 = 3$ **29** $\dfrac{m}{2} = 2$ **30** $\dfrac{n}{6} = 2$

31 $\dfrac{p}{6} = 2$ **32** $\dfrac{q}{5} = 3$ **33** $\dfrac{16}{y} = 8$

You can also use algebra to solve equations with more than one operation.

Example 10

Solve $3p + 2 = 20$
Subtract 2 from both sides:

$$3p + 2 - 2 = 20 - 2$$
$$3p = 18$$

Divide both sides by 3:

$$3p \div 3 = 18 \div 3$$
$$p = 6$$

Remember:
Always do the same
to both sides to
make sure the
equation balances.

Example 11

Solve $4p - 2 = 10$
Add 2 to both sides:

$$4p - 2 + 2 = 10 + 2$$
$$4p = 12$$

Divide both sides by 4:

$$4p \div 4 = 12 \div 4$$
$$p = 3$$

Exercise 13H

Use algebra to solve these equations:

1 $3a + 5 = 14$ **2** $2b + 5 = 9$ **3** $4c + 8 = 12$
4 $5d + 8 = 28$ **5** $2e - 1 = 5$ **6** $3f - 6 = 15$
7 $2g - 6 = 12$ **8** $5h - 11 = 9$ **9** $5i + 1 = 26$

10 $6j + 8 = 26$ **11** $2k + 12 = 26$ **12** $2l + 5 = 21$
13 $3m - 6 = 12$ **14** $2n - 12 = 12$ **15** $5p - 22 = 8$
16 $7q - 4 = 31$ **17** $2r + 18 = 26$ **18** $5s + 3 = 23$
19 $10t + 15 = 35$ **20** $12u + 8 = 32$ **21** $6v - 16 = 20$
22 $5w - 5 = 15$ **23** $2x - 6 = 4$ **24** $2y - 7 = 6$

Summary of key points

Equation:

$$x + 4 = 7$$

This is only true when $x = 3$
The **solution** to this
equation is $x = 3$

Formula:

Pay = hours worked × rate of pay
$$P = h \times r$$

This works for many different
values of h and r.

14 Perimeter, area and volume

14.1 Perimeter and area

Mrs Malloy has laid a patio.
She used square slabs with one metre sides.

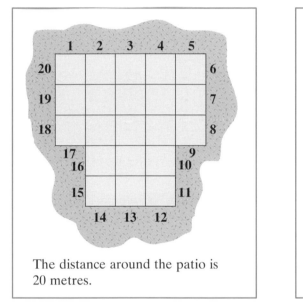

The distance around the patio is
20 metres.

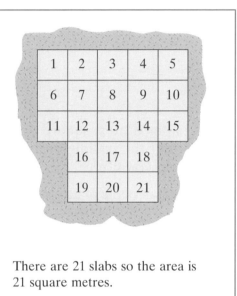

There are 21 slabs so the area is
21 square metres.

- ■ **The distance around a flat shape is the perimeter.**
- ■ **The amount of space that a shape covers is the area.**

Example 1

Work out the perimeter and
area of this shape drawn on
centimetre squared paper.

There are 24 one centimetre edges
so the perimeter is 24 cm.
There are 27 centimetre squares
so the area is 27 cm^2.

Exercise 14A

1   These shapes have been drawn on cm² paper.
    Find the perimeter and area of each shape.

Remember:
cm² is short for
'square centimetres'
or 'centimetres
squared'.

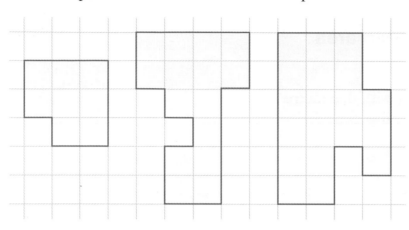

2   On cm² paper draw a square with sides of 4 cm.
    (a) Work out the perimeter and area of the square.
    (b) What do you notice?

3   This shape has been made from centimetre squares.

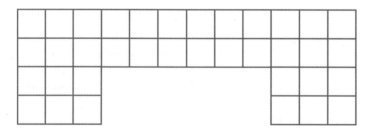

    (a) Work out the perimeter and area.
    (b) Rearrange the shape into a square.
    (c) Find the perimeter of the square.

Example 2

Find the perimeter of this triangle:

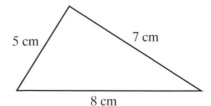

The perimeter is the distance around a shape.
The perimeter of the triangle is:

$$7 + 5 + 8 = 20 \, cm$$

Exercise 14B

1 Work out the perimeters of these shapes.

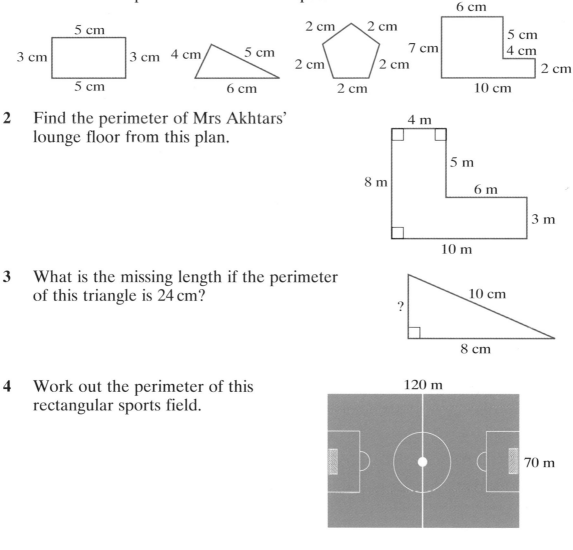

2 Find the perimeter of Mrs Akhtars' lounge floor from this plan.

3 What is the missing length if the perimeter of this triangle is 24 cm?

4 Work out the perimeter of this rectangular sports field.

14.2 Formulae for the perimeter and area of a rectangle

The perimeter of this rectangle is:

$$5 + 5 + 3 + 3 = 16 \text{ cm}$$

Which is the same as:

$$2 \times 5 + 2 \times 3 = 16 \text{ cm}$$

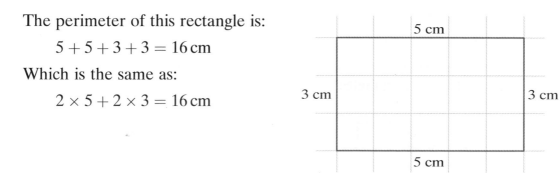

■ **The perimeter of a rectangle is:**

$$\textbf{perimeter} = \textbf{2} \times \textbf{length} + \textbf{2} \times \textbf{width}$$
$$= \textbf{2} \times \textbf{(length + width)}$$

You can find the area of any rectangle . . .

. . . by counting squares   . . . by using a formula

1	2	3	4	5
6	7	8	9	10
11	12	13	14	15

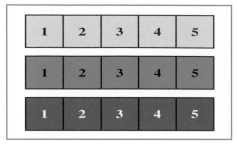

By counting squares the area of this rectangle is 15 cm.

The rectangle has 3 rows of 5 squares. The area is the total number of squares: $3 \times 5 = 15\,\text{cm}^2$.

■ **The area of a rectangle is:**

$$\textbf{area} = \textbf{length} \times \textbf{width}$$

Example 3

Use the formulae to work out:
(a) the perimeter   **(b)** the area of this carpet.

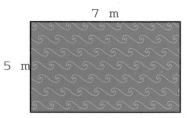

7 m

5 m

(a) Perimeter is $2 \times \text{length} + 2 \times \text{width}$
$$= 2 \times 7 + 2 \times 5$$
$$= 24\,\text{m}$$

(b) Area is $\text{length} \times \text{width}$
$$= 7 \times 5$$
$$= 35\,\text{m}^2$$

Exercise 14C

1   Use the formulae to work out the perimeter and the area of each of these rectangles.

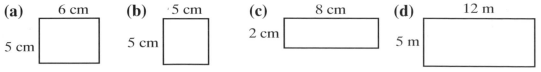

(a) 6 cm 5 cm   **(b)** 5 cm 5 cm   **(c)** 8 cm 2 cm   **(d)** 12 m 5 m

2   Work out:
(a) the perimeter, and
(b) the area of this rectangle.

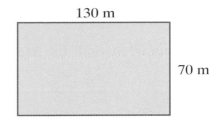

3   Here are a square and a rectangle:

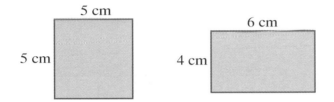

Which of these two shapes has:
(a) the greatest perimeter?
(b) the greatest area?

4   Find the area of this L-shaped floor space.

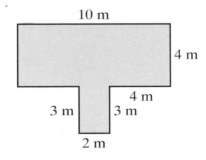

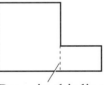

Draw in this line
to help you.

5   The Murphy family have a patio in the shape of a T:

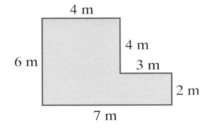

Work out:
(a) the perimeter of the patio
(b) the area of the patio.

6   The perimeter of a rectangle is 22 cm.
The length of the rectangle is 8 cm.
Find its area.

14.3 The area of a triangle

Any triangle is half the area of its surrounding rectangle:

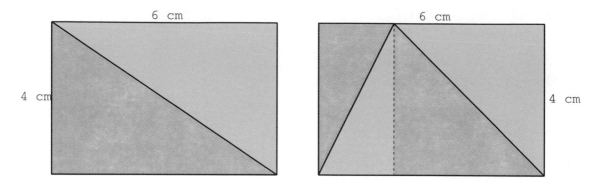

In both cases the red area is the same as the blue area.

In each case:
Area of surrounding rectangle is $6 \times 4 = 24 \, \text{cm}^2$.
So the area of each triangle is $\frac{1}{2}$ of $24 = 12 \, \text{cm}^2$.

For any triangle:

Area of triangle is $\frac{1}{2}$ area of surrounding rectangle

Area of surrounding rectangle is base × height

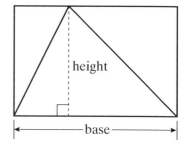

■ **The area of a triangle is:**

area $= \frac{1}{2} \times$ base $\times$ height

Example 4

Find the area of this triangle.

Using the formula:

$$\text{area} = \frac{1}{2} \times \text{base} \times \text{height}$$
$$= \frac{1}{2} \times 10 \times 6$$
$$= \frac{1}{2} \times 60$$
$$= 30 \, \text{cm}^2$$

Exercise 14D

1 Work out the area of each of these triangles:

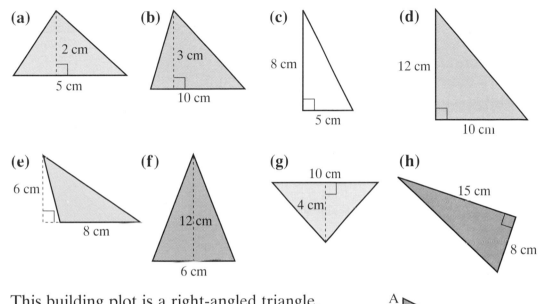

(a) 2 cm, 5 cm

(b) 3 cm, 10 cm

(c) 8 cm, 5 cm

(d) 12 cm, 10 cm

(e) 6 cm, 8 cm

(f) 12 cm, 6 cm

(g) 10 cm, 4 cm

(h) 15 cm, 8 cm

2 This building plot is a right-angled triangle.
AB = 30 m, BC = 60 m and the angle at B = 90°.
Calculate the area of the plot.

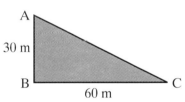

A
30 m
B
60 m
C

3 Which of these two shapes has the larger area, and by
how much?

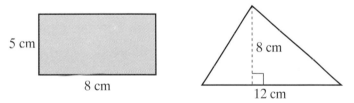

5 cm, 8 cm

8 cm, 12 cm

4 Work out the area of the shaded region.

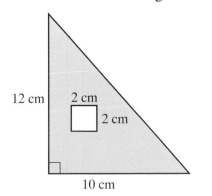

12 cm, 2 cm, 2 cm, 10 cm

5 Kirk cuts a triangle from the corner of a square piece of card.
Work out the area of:
(a) the triangle
(b) the remaining piece of the square.

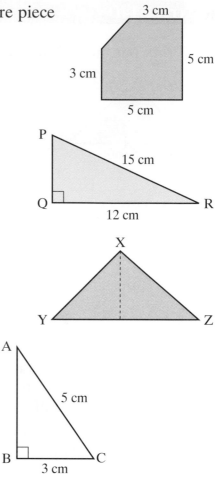

6 The perimeter of this triangle is 36 cm.
Work out:
(a) the length of PQ
(b) the area of the triangle.

7 The area of this triangle is 25 cm^2.
The height of the triangle is 5 cm.
Work out length of the base YZ.

8 The area of this triangle is 6 cm^2.
Work out the perimeter of the triangle.

14.4 Composite shapes

Here are two ways of finding the area of more complicated shapes:

Method 1

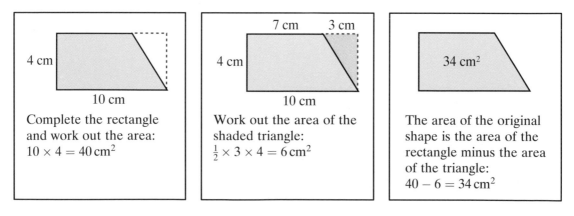

Complete the rectangle and work out the area:
$10 \times 4 = 40$ cm^2

Work out the area of the shaded triangle:
$\frac{1}{2} \times 3 \times 4 = 6$ cm^2

The area of the original shape is the area of the rectangle minus the area of the triangle:
$40 - 6 = 34$ cm^2

Method 2

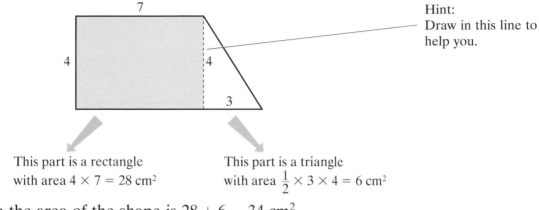

This part is a rectangle
with area 4 × 7 = 28 cm²

This part is a triangle
with area $\frac{1}{2}$ × 3 × 4 = 6 cm²

Hint:
Draw in this line to
help you.

So the area of the shape is $28 + 6 = 34$ cm².

Exercise 14E

1 Use each method to find the area of this shape.
Make sure you get the same answer with both.

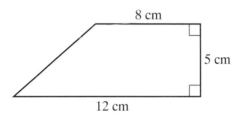

2 Work out the areas of these shapes.
Try using both methods to see which you prefer.

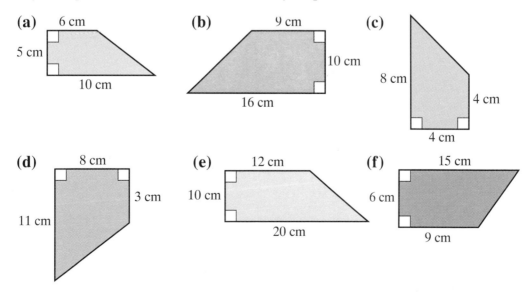

14.5 The area of a parallelogram

A parallelogram is a four-sided shape with two sets of parallel sides.

To find its area you make it into a rectangle:

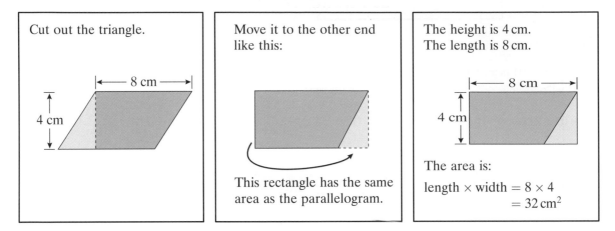

Cut out the triangle.

8 cm

4 cm

Move it to the other end like this:

This rectangle has the same area as the parallelogram.

The height is 4 cm.
The length is 8 cm.

8 cm

4 cm

The area is:

length × width = 8 × 4
= 32 cm²

■ **The area of a parallelogram is: area = length × width**

Example 5

Work out the area of this parallelogram.

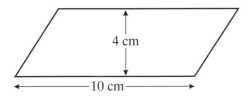

4 cm

10 cm

Length = 10 cm

Width = 4 cm

So using the formula:

$$area = length \times width$$
$$= 10\,cm \times 4\,cm$$
$$= 40\,cm^2$$

Exercise 14F

Work out the area of each of these parallelograms.

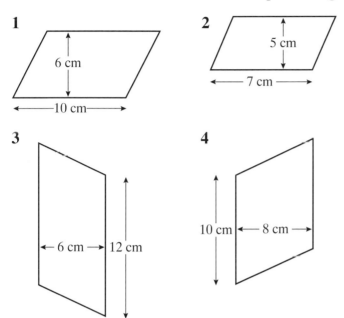

1 6 cm, 10 cm

2 5 cm, 7 cm

3 6 cm, 12 cm

4 10 cm, 8 cm

14.6 The circumference of a circle

The circumference of a circle is related to its diameter.

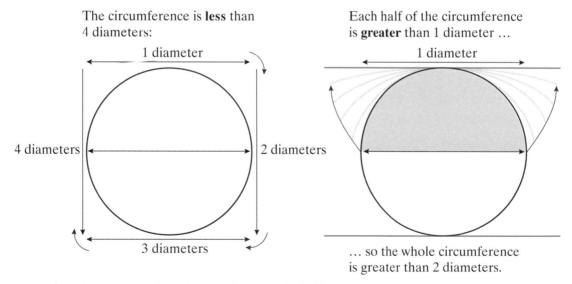

The circumference is **less** than 4 diameters:

1 diameter

4 diameters   2 diameters

3 diameters

Each half of the circumference is **greater** than 1 diameter …

1 diameter

… so the whole circumference is greater than 2 diameters.

A good estimate for the circumference is 3 diameters
– in between 4 and 2 diameters.

Example 6

Check that a circle with a diameter of 4 cm has a circumference of about $3 \times 4 = 12$ cm.

Draw the circle on cm² paper and mark points 1 cm apart around it:

Join the points together to form a shape with a perimeter just less than the circle:

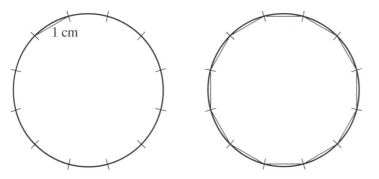

The perimeter of the shape is just over 12 cm.
So $3 \times$ diameter $= 3 \times 4 = 12$ cm is a good estimate for the circumference of this circle.

Exercise 14G

1   Repeat the process in Example 6 for circles with a diameter of:

    (a) 3 cm   **(b)** 5 cm.

14.7 Introducing π

You have seen that the circumference of a circle is about 3 times its diameter. The actual circumference is:

circumference $= \pi \times$ diameter

π is the number you get if you divide the circumference of any circle by its diameter. It is the same value for any circle.

The value of π is about 3.14.

π is a Greek letter and it is pronounced 'pie'.

■   **The circumference of a circle is:**

$$\textbf{circumference} = \boldsymbol{\pi} \times \textbf{diameter} = \boldsymbol{\pi} \times \textbf{2} \times \textbf{radius}$$

$$= \textbf{2} \times \boldsymbol{\pi} \times \textbf{radius}$$

Use your calculator to find the value of π to several decimal places.

Example 7

Work out the circumference of a circle of radius 5 cm.

$$\text{Circumference} = 2 \times \pi \times \text{radius}$$
$$= 2 \times \pi \times 5$$
$$= 2 \times 3.14 \times 5$$

So circumference $= 31.4$ cm

Exercise 14H

1   Find the circumference of a circle of radius:
    (a) 4 cm   **(b)** 3 cm   **(c)** 6 cm   **(d)** 2.5 cm

2   Find the circumference of a circle with radius:
    (a) 3 m   **(b)** 5 m   **(c)** 2.8 m   **(d)** 15 m

3   The radius of the circle at the centre
    of a sports field is 10 m. Work out
    the circumference of the circle.

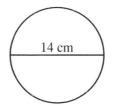

4   Find the circumference of this circle:

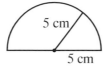

5   Find the total distance around this semicircle:

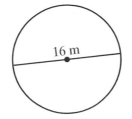

6   What is the circumference of this circle?

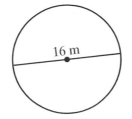

7 Work out the circumference of a circle of diameter:
   (a) 10 cm   **(b)** 12 cm   **(c)** 15 cm   **(d)** 22 cm

8 Find the total distance around this table mat.

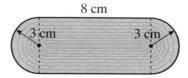

9 This church door is a rectangle with a semicircle at the top. Find its perimeter.

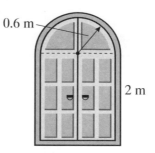

14.8 Estimating the area of a circle

You can estimate the area of a circle, like this:

This square is made from 8 equal triangles:

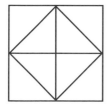

The area of the circle is greater than 4 triangles …

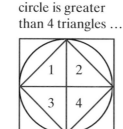

… but less than 8 triangles.

The area of the circle is more than half the square (4 triangles), but less than the whole square (8 triangles).

A good estimate for the area of the circle is $\frac{3}{4}$ of the area of the surrounding square.

Example 8

Estimate the area of a circle with a radius of 5 cm.

Draw the surrounding square.
It has sides of 10 cm.

The area of the square is $10 \times 10 = 100 \text{ cm}^2$.
So a good estimate for the area of the circle is:

$$\frac{3}{4} \times 100 = 75 \text{ cm}^2$$

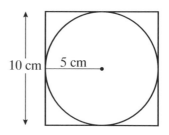

Exercise 14I

1   Estimate the area of each circle:

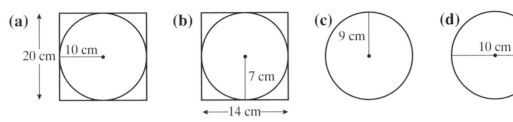

(a) 20 cm   10 cm

(b) 7 cm   ←—14 cm—→

(c) 9 cm

(d) 10 cm

2   Activity

You will need Activity Sheet 3.

• Estimate the area of each circle, as in question 1
• Follow the instructions on the sheet to work out the area of the circle

This shows that the estimate you have been using is very close to the actual area of the circle.

14.9 As easy as pi

You can rearrange the sectors of the circle into a rectangle like this:

The thinner the sectors get, the closer the shape gets to a rectangle:

$\frac{1}{2}$ circumference

radius

Its area is the same as the circle.

Each side is roughly half the circumference …

… and the width is roughly 1 radius

The area of the rectangle is:

  half the circumference (length) × radius (width)

    $\pi \times$ radius   × radius

or $\pi \times$ radius^2

■ **The area of a circle is:**

  area $= \pi \times$ radius^2

Hint:
The circumference of a circle is:

$2 \times \pi \times$ radius,

so half the circumference is:

$\pi \times$ radius.

Exercise 14J

1 Work out the area of a circle of radius:

   (a) 5 cm   **(b)** 6 cm

   (c) 8 cm   **(d)** 10 cm

2 Work out the area of each of these circles:

   (a)   **(b)**

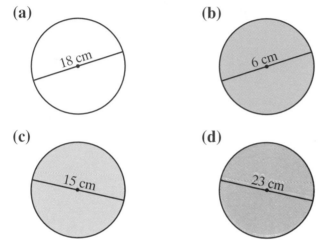

   (c)   **(d)**

3 Mr Quy has a rug with a diameter of 10 m.
Work out the area of the rug.

4 Which has the greatest area and by how much:

   (a) A square of side 5 cm or a circle of radius 3 cm

   (b) A rectangle which measures 4 cm by 8 cm or a
      circle of radius 5 cm.

5 Mrs Lewis has a circular mat with a diameter of
3 metres.
Work out the area of the mat.

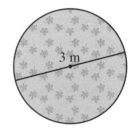

6 Work out the area of this semicircle.

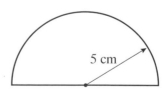

7 Find the area of this church door.

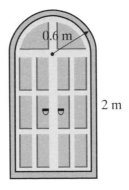

Hint:
split the door into a
rectangle and a
semicircle

8 Work out the area of this sports field.

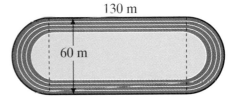

9 Find the area of the shaded ring.

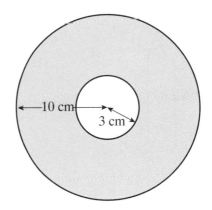

10 This shape is made from a rectangle with a semicircle
cut out of one end.
Work out the area of the shape.

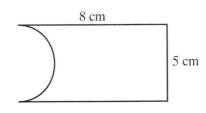

11 Joan cuts a circle of radius 3 cm from
a sheet of card.

Work out the area of:
(a) the sheet of card
(b) the circle that has been cut out
(c) the remaining piece of the card.

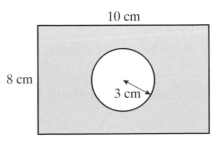

14.10 The volume of a cuboid

Solid and hollow shapes take up space in three dimensions. They are called 3-dimensional shapes.

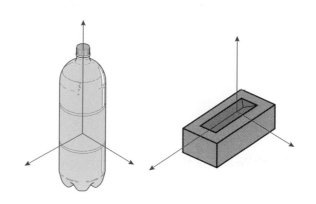

■ **The volume is the amount of space taken up by a 3-dimensional shape.**

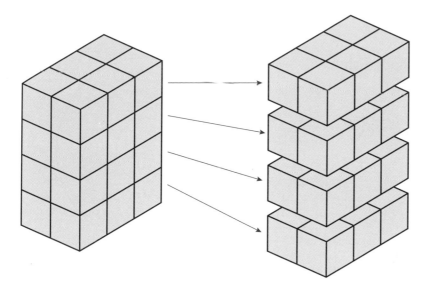

This cuboid is made from centimetre cubes. Each cube has a volume of 1 cm³ or 1 cubic centimetre.

There are 4 layers of 6 cubes each.

remember:

1 cm³ means 'one cubic centimetre', or 'one centimetre cubed'.

The total number of cubes is

4 layers of 2×3 cubes $= 4 \times 6$

$= 24$ cubes

So the volume of the cuboid is 24 cm³.

■ **The volume of a cuboid is:**

volume = length × width × height

Example 9

Work out the volume of this cuboid.

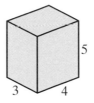

Length = 3 cm   width = 4 cm   height = 5 cm

So using the formula:

volume = length × width × height

the volume is:

volume = 3 × 4 × 5

= 60 cm³

Exercise 14K

1   Find the volume of each of these cuboids:

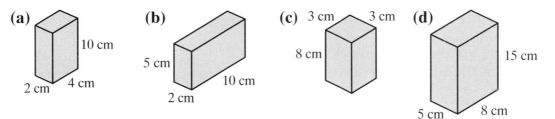

(a) 10 cm, 2 cm, 4 cm

(b) 5 cm, 10 cm, 2 cm

(c) 3 cm, 3 cm, 8 cm

(d) 15 cm, 5 cm, 8 cm

2   A block of wood is a cuboid, with length = 12 cm,
width = 5 cm, height = 3 cm.
Find the volume of the block.

3   Nikki's filing cabinet is a cuboid.
The base is a square of side 30 cm and the
height is 80 cm.
Work out the volume of the filing cabinet.

4   Find the volume of a cube with sides of 4 cm.

5 The volume of this cuboid is 150 cm³.
Work out its height.

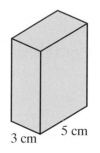

3 cm   5 cm

6 Aleya's bedroom is a cuboid.
The floor is a rectangle 4 metres by 3.5 metres.
Find the volume if the height of the room is 2.5 metres.

7 These speakers are cuboids.
The sides are 28 cm, 14 cm and 20 cm.
Work out the total volume of the two
speakers.

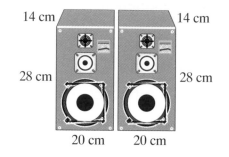

14 cm   14 cm
28 cm   28 cm
20 cm   20 cm

8 A metal cube has sides of 6 cm.
The cube is melted down and reformed as a cuboid
with length 12 cm and width 6 cm.
Find the height of the new cuboid.

9 What volume of this block of wood is left
when the smaller part is cut off?

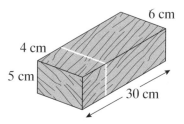

6 cm
4 cm
5 cm
30 cm

14.11 The volume of a prism

A cuboid is a prism with a rectangular base.

Here are some other prisms:

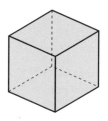

Triangular-based   Hexagonal-based   Pentagonal-based

The formula for the volume of a cuboid is

volume = length × width × height

Length × width is the area of the rectangular base, so

volume = area of base × height

■   **The volume of a prism is:**

volume = area of base × height

Example 10

Find the volume of this prism.

There are two methods you can use.

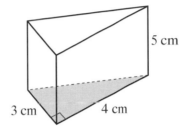

Method 1

The prism is half of this cuboid:

The volume of the cuboid is

length × width × height = $3 \times 4 \times 5 = 60\,\text{cm}^3$

The volume of the cuboid is

$\frac{1}{2}$ the volume of the prism $= \frac{1}{2} \times 60$

$= 30\,\text{cm}^3$

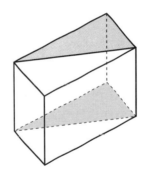

Method 2

Use the formula:

volume = area of the base × height

The area of the base is $\frac{1}{2}$ × base × height

$= \frac{1}{2} \times 4 \times 3$

$= \frac{1}{2} \times 12 = 6\,\text{cm}^2$

So the volume of the prism is

area of base × height $= 6 \times 5$

$= 30\,\text{cm}^3$

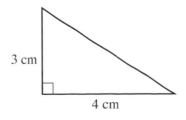

Exercise 14L

1   For each prism:
    (i) work out the area of the base
    (ii) use the formula to work out the volume.

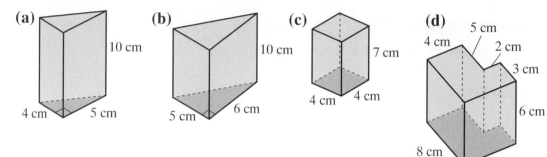

(a)   10 cm   4 cm   5 cm

(b)   10 cm   5 cm   6 cm

(c)   7 cm   4 cm   4 cm

(d)   5 cm   4 cm   2 cm   3 cm   6 cm   8 cm   6 cm

2   Work out the volumes of these prisms.

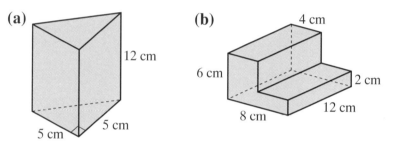

(a)   12 cm   5 cm   5 cm

(b)   4 cm   6 cm   2 cm   8 cm   12 cm

3   The diagram shows a wedge which is used as a doorstop.
    Work out the volume of the wedge.

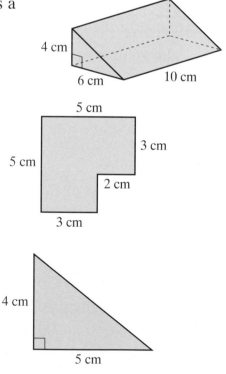

4 cm   6 cm   10 cm

4   The diagram shows the base of a prism.
    The height of the prism is 10 cm.

    Work out the volume of the prism.

5 cm   3 cm   5 cm   2 cm   3 cm

5   The diagram shows the base of a prism.
    The volume of this prism is 180 cm^3.

    Work out the height of the prism.

4 cm   5 cm

6 The diagrams show the end face of a prism and the whole prism.

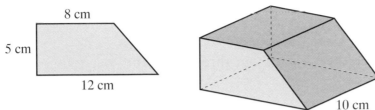

8 cm

5 cm

12 cm

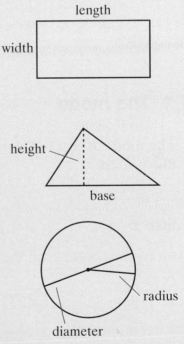

10 cm

Work out:
(a) the area of the end face
(b) the volume of the prism.

Summary of key points

1 The distance around a flat shape is the perimeter.

2 The amount of space that a shape covers is the area.

3 The perimeter of a rectangle is:
$$\text{perimeter} = 2 \times \text{length} + 2 \times \text{width}$$
$$= 2 \times (\text{length} + \text{width})$$

length

width

4 The area of a rectangle is:
$$\text{area} = \text{length} \times \text{width}$$

5 The area of a triangle is:
$$\text{area} = \tfrac{1}{2} \times \text{base} \times \text{height}$$

height

base

6 The area of a parallelogram is:
$$\text{area} = \text{base} \times \text{height}$$

7 The circumference of a circle is:
$$\text{circumference} = \pi \times \text{diameter}$$
$$= \pi \times 2 \times \text{radius}$$

radius

8 The area of a circle is:
$$\text{area} = \pi \times \text{radius}^2$$

diameter

9 The volume is the amount of space taken up by a 3-dimensional shape.

10 The volume of a cuboid is:
$$\text{volume} = \text{length} \times \text{width} \times \text{height}$$

11 The volume of a prism is:
$$\text{volume} = \text{area of base} \times \text{height}$$

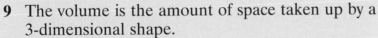

15 Averages

This chapter will show you how to work out three different averages:

The mode:

Brown is the most common eye colour.

The median:

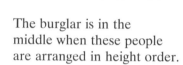

The burglar is in the middle when these people are arranged in height order.

The mean:

"Tonight's five lucky winners will share the one million pound jackpot"

"WOW, that's £200 000 each!"

£1 000 000 ÷ 5 = £200 000

You can use these averages to compare different sets of data.

15.1 The mode

■ **The mode of a set of data is the value which occurs most often.**

Example 1

Eleven friends compared the number of CDs they bought in one year:

   3, 6, 1, 8, 4, 7, 3, 5, 3, 4, 3

What is the mode?

The number which occurs most often is 3.
So the mode is 3 CDs.

You can also say the modal number of CDs is 3

Mode facts:
- There can be more than 1 mode.
- Sometimes there is no mode.
- The mode does not have to be a number.

Example 2

These numbers show how often a group of children visit the dentist in one year:

Fred went twice

1, 2, 2, 1, 0, 3, 0, 2, 1, 5

June went 3 times

This data has 2 modes.

Find the mode for the data.

The mode is both 1 **and** 2 because both numbers appear three times.

Example 3

This table shows the colour of 10 cars.

Ford	VW	Ford	Seat	Rover	VW	Citroen	Rover	Ford	BMW
green	blue	red	blue	white	black	green	blue	red	black

Find **(a)** the modal make of car
   (b) the modal colour of car.

(a) The modal make of car is Ford.
(b) The modal colour is blue.

Example 4

Here are twelve car registration numbers:

   112, 236, 344,179, 736, 615, 123, 998, 101, 314, 253, 641

Find the mode.

All the numbers appear once only so there is no mode.

Exercise 15A

1   The number of spelling mistakes made by John in 12 essays is shown below:

      1, 3, 2, 7, 3, 5, 0, 1, 3, 1, 3, 3

Work out the mode for the number of spelling mistakes.

2 Kay's scores for different subjects are shown below. Write down the modes for each subject.

English 6, 8, 5, 6, 8, 3, 5, 6, 9, 10, 8
French 12, 12, 11, 8, 7, 8, 11, 5, 8, 10
Maths 23, 24, 15, 23, 36, 18, 25, 36, 23
History 3, 5, 7, 9, 3, 5, 3, 10, 9, 6

3 Here are the number of goals scored by 2 football teams.

Manchester Rovers 1 3 1 2 1 4 5 2 2 1
Leeds Athletic 1 2 2 2 4 3 1 1 2 0

(a) Work out the mode for the number of goals scored for each club.
(b) Which club had the larger mode?

4 Here are the shoe sizes of the children in a Year 8 class.

9, 10, 4, 5, 6, 3, 6, 12, 6, 4, 6, 9, 7, 10, 6, 6, 7, 6, 5, 8, 10, 3, 5, 6, 8, 3, 8, 5, 6

What is the modal shoe size?

15.2 Using a chart or table to find the mode

It is easy to find the mode from a bar chart.

■ **In a bar chart the mode is the value with the highest bar.**

Example 5

This bar chart shows how many TVs each household has:

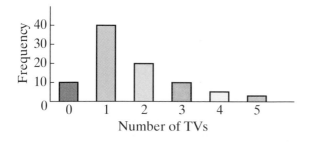

So the mode is 1 TV.

■ **In a frequency table, the mode is the value with the highest frequency.**

Example 6

Rashida throws a pair of dice 36 times and she records her scores.

2	4	7	9	10	8	7	8	7
6	7	10	7	9	3	4	5	3
12	6	6	10	9	8	8	4	5
6	11	5	6	5	3	7	7	7

She completes a frequency table:

Score	Tally	Frequency
2	|	1
3	||	2
4	|||	3
5	⊥⊦⊦⊤	5
6	⊥⊦⊦⊤	5
7	⊥⊦⊦⊤ |||	8
8	||||	4
9	|||	3
10	|||	3
11	|	1
12	|	1

The score which occurs the most has the highest frequency.

So Rashida's mode is a score of 7.

Exercise 15B

1   This bar chart shows the goals scored by a football team in each game in one season:

Write down the modal number of goals scored.

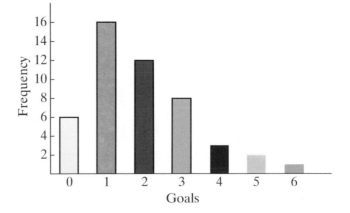

2   Kiesha records the shoe size for the pupils in her class.
     She draws a bar chart to show her results:

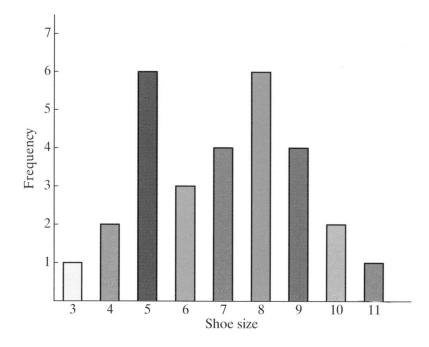

     Write down the 2 modes for this data.

3   The table shows how late trains arrived at Birmingham
     station one day.

No. of mins late	0	1	2	3	4	5	6
Frequency	12	56	34	20	12	23	9

     Work out the mode for the number of minutes late.

4   From this graph, write down the modal number of
     goals scored.

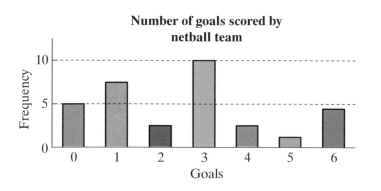

15.3 The median

■ **The median is the middle value when the data is arranged in order of size.**

Example 7

The heights of five girls are:

Candice	156 cm
Anne	164 cm
Rashida	140 cm
Georgina	152 cm
Sarah	178 cm

Find the median height.

To find the median, arrange the heights in order and find the middle value.

140   152   156   164   178

middle value

So the median height is 156 cm.

Example 8

The ages of 12 relatives are:

32, 45, 15, 29, 13, 34, 56, 30, 51, 15

Work out the median age.

First arrange the ages in order:

13,   15,   15,   29,   ⟨30⟩,   ⟨32⟩,   34,   45,   51,   56

2 middle values

Remember to write 15 twice.

To find the median, add the 2 middle values and divide by 2:

$$\text{median} = \frac{30 + 32}{2} = 31$$

so the median age is 31.

Exercise 15C

1   Arrange the following sets of data in order and find the median:
    (a) 2, 5, 7, 11, 5, 9, 8
    (b) £1, £8, £9, £3, £7, £12, £1, £8
    (c) 12 kg, 10 kg, 9 kg, 14 kg, 20 kg, 16 kg, 10 kg, 8 kg, 9 kg, 11 kg

2   Jo completes three tests in Science, English and Maths. Her marks for each question are:

    Science   12, 14, 5, 12, 13, 10, 12, 14, 18, 9, 10, 10, 12, 13, 13
    English   12, 15, 9, 12, 13, 2, 5, 10, 11, 23
    Maths   21, 33, 15, 30, 15

    (a) Work out the median mark for each subject.
    (b) Which subject had the largest median?
    (c) Work out the median mark for all the marks.

3   Anwar counts the number of lorries which pass by his school on the motorway every five minutes during a lesson.

    11, 7, 8, 1, 5, 3, 1, 5, 6, 1, 12, 3

    Work out the median number of lorries.

4   An eight-sided dice is thrown 20 times. Here are the results:

    3, 2, 6, 7, 3, 1, 8, 4, 3, 5, 6, 2, 7, 1, 6, 8, 3, 2, 5, 1

    (a) Calculate the median.
    (b) Work out the mode.

5   Find the median of Dijana's maths test marks for last year.

    Marks: 40% 75% 70% 56% 39% 50% 69% 65% 65%

15.4 The mean

The mean is the sum of all the values divided by the number of values.

■ **Mean** $= \dfrac{\textbf{sum of values}}{\textbf{number of values}}$

Example 9

1   The number of children on 9 UKAir flights is:

   1, 5, 3, 2, 8, 4, 3, 5, 5

   Work out the mean number of children on a UKAir flight.

   Sum of values $= 1 + 5 + 3 + 2 + 8 + 4 + 3 + 5 + 5$
   $= 36$

   There are 9 values so:

   $\text{Mean} = \dfrac{36}{9}$
   $= 4$

   The mean is 4 children.

2   For Virgo Atlantis, the number of children for 10 flights is:

   2, 3, 3, 1, 0, 1, 1, 4, 4, 3

   Work out the mean.

   The sum of the values $= 2 + 3 + 3 + 1 + 0 + 1 + 1 + 4 + 4 + 3$
   $= 22$

   There are 10 values so:

   $\text{Mean} = \dfrac{22}{10}$
   $= 2.2$

   The mean does not have to be a whole number.

   The mean is 2.2 children.

Exercise 15D

1   Find the mean for these sets of data:
    (a) 2, 4, 6, 7, 9, 12, 15, 19, 11, 15
    (b) £1, £8, £11, £2, £5, £1, £1, £3, £4, £12, £9, £6
    (c) 12 kg, 10 kg, 9 kg, 14 kg, 20 kg, 16 kg, 10 kg, 8 kg

2   Kate takes three tests in maths, science and English.
    Her marks for each question are:

    Maths   21, 33, 15, 24, 36, 45, 56, 64
    Science   12, 15, 9, 12, 13, 2, 5, 10, 13, 15
    English   2, 4, 8, 1, 0, 3, 12, 6, 5, 2, 1, 3, 0, 3, 4

    Work out the mean mark for each subject.

3   Rachel scores 156 runs in eight cricket innings.
    Work out her mean number of runs per innings.

4   The number of goals scored by two football teams in
    five matches is:

Kilbride Rovers	2	0	1	2	0
Fife United	3	1	2	3	1

    (a) What is the mean number of goals for each team?
    (b) Which team has the highest mean?

5   Levi gets these results in her maths tests:

    18, 15, 19, 16, 14, 20

    (a) What is her mean mark?
    (b) What mark must Levi get in her next test to get a
    mean mark of 16?

15.5 The range

The range of a set of data tells you how spread out the data
is.
The range is the difference between the highest and lowest
value in your data:

■   **Range = highest value − lowest value**

Example 10

Nadine and Rochelle compare their marks for maths homeworks:

Nadine	7	18	20	5	12
Rochelle	16	17	16	15	16

Calculate the range of marks for each student.

Range = highest mark − lowest mark

For Nadine:

range = 20 − 5 = 15

For Rochelle:

range = 17 − 15 = 2

Rochelle's marks were more consistent because they are less spread out.

Exercise 15E

1   Jody's marks for 10 geography homeworks are:

13, 16, 14, 8, 11, 14, 10, 17, 11, 15

Work out the range of her marks.

2   The temperatures in 6 cities were:

11 °C, 5 °C, 14 °C, −3 °C, 0 °C, 8 °C

What is the range of these temperatures?

3   The top mark in the half-term test for Class 7 was 82%.
The range of the marks was 40%.
What was the lowest mark in the test?

4   At the end of the season, the team at the bottom of the league had scored 28 points.
If the range of points is 54, how many points did the team at the top of the league have?

15.6 Finding the mean from frequency tables

You can use a frequency table to work out the mean:

Example 11

This table shows the number of children in different families:

Number of children	Frequency
0	4
1	9
2	6
3	2
4	3
5	1

This means that 3 families have 4 children.

$$\text{Mean} = \frac{\text{total number of children}}{\text{total frequency}}$$

Re-draw the table to find the total number of children:

Number of children	Frequency	Number of children × Frequency
0	4	$0 \times 4 = 0$
1	9	$1 \times 9 = 9$
2	6	$2 \times 6 = 12$
3	2	$3 \times 2 = 6$
4	3	$4 \times 3 = 12$
5	1	$5 \times 1 = 5$
Total frequency =	25	Total number of children 44

Add a new column.

Remember, when using a frequency table:
$$\text{mean} = \frac{\text{total of (each value} \times \text{frequency)}}{\text{total frequency}}$$

This tells us the total number of families.

$$\text{Mean} = \frac{\text{total number of children}}{\text{total frequency}} = \frac{44}{25}$$

Mean = 1.76 children

This means that the mean number of children per family is 1.76.

Exercise 15F

1 Imoen throws a dice 60 times. The results are shown in the table.

Number rolled	Frequency	Score frequency
1	7	
2	11	
3	10	
4	13	
5	9	
6	10	
Total frequency =		Total score =

Hint:
Start by adding a new column.

Find the total score and the mean score

2 The ages of 500 children in a school are shown in the table.

Age in years	Frequency	Age × Frequency
11	85	
12	92	
13	103	
14	98	
15	89	
16	33	
Total frequency =		Total number of years =

Complete the table and work out the mean age.

3 For the following sets of data work out:
   (a) the mode
   (b) the median
   (c) the mean
   (d) the range.
       (i)   5, 3, 5, 7, 5, 1, 8, 9, 10, 12
       (ii) £12, £32, £15, £12, £30
       (iii) 1.8, 2.3, 5.6, 1.8, 3.5, 2.3, 4.5, 1.9, 2.7, 4.1

4 The number of house sales an estate agent makes per month is shown in the table.

Month	Jan	Feb	Mar	Apr	May	Jun	Jul	Aug	Sept	Oct	Nov	Dec
Number of sales	8	12	23	15	20	12	25	12	21	18	15	12

For this data, calculate:

(a) the mean   **(b)** the median

(c) the mode   **(d)** the range.

5 Jaz throws a pair of dice 25 times. His scores are:

2, 7, 6, 8, 9, 10, 11, 3, 2, 5, 8, 6, 9
12, 10, 8, 4, 3, 11, 12, 9, 10, 6, 7, 8

For this data, calculate:

(a) the mean   **(b)** the median

(c) the mode   **(d)** the range.

6 Sally writes down the number of strikes she makes when she goes ten pin bowling. Her results for 60 games are:

0, 3, 5, 3, 2, 6, 4, 2, 4, 5, 8, 3, 2, 1, 0, 2, 5, 3, 0, 3, 5,
3, 6, 3, 5, 2, 1, 4, 3, 3, 6, 3, 9, 9, 3, 5, 2, 5, 7, 5, 1, 6,
4, 3, 7, 3, 2, 4, 5, 3, 7, 1, 7, 3, 4, 3, 7, 6, 8, 1

(a) Copy and complete the following frequency table:

Number of strikes	Tally	Frequency
0		
1		
2		
3		
4		
5		
6		
7		
8		
9		

(b) Work out the modal number of strikes.

(c) Work out the mean number of strikes.

7 The table shows the number of eggs in 40 birds nests:

Number of eggs	Frequency	Number of eggs × frequency
0	3	$0 \times 3 = 0$
1	2	$1 \times 2 =$
2	5	
3	8	
4	12	
5	6	
6	4	

Copy this table and fill in the missing spaces.

Use the table to find:

(a) the modal number of eggs

(b) the mean number of eggs.

15.7 Comparing data

You can use the mean and range to compare different sets of data.

Emma and Lucy compared their science homework marks.

Week:	1	2	3	4	5
Emma	16	15	16	18	15
Lucy	11	15	20	10	14

The mean marks are:

Emma: $\dfrac{16 + 15 + 16 + 18 + 15}{5} = \dfrac{80}{5} = 16$

Lucy: $\dfrac{11 + 15 + 20 + 10 + 14}{5} = \dfrac{70}{5} = 14$

So Emma's mean mark is higher than Lucy's.

The range of Emma's marks is:

range = highest mark − lowest mark

$= 18 - 15 = 3$

The range of Lucy's marks is:

range = highest mark − lowest mark

= 20 − 10 = 10

Emma's range is lower. Her marks are less spread out.
Lucy has some high marks but also some low ones. Her
marks are more spread out.
Overall, it is Emma who did better.

Exercise 15G

1   Liam and Seb play cricket. Their scores for eleven
    innings last season were:

Liam	32	37	44	39	39	41	36	45	30	38	45
Seb	7	58	15	1	46	10	50	65	45	46	52

   (a) Work out:
       (i)   the mean number of runs scored by each
             player
       (ii) the range of scores for each player.
   (b) Comment on who has done best.

2   Cristo, Mary and Jessica each do ten spelling tests.
    Cristo's mean mark is 13 with a range of 3.
    Mary's mean mark is 9 with a range of 2.
    Jessica's mean mark is 8 with a range of 12.

    Comment on who did best and worst on the tests.

3   Aleyha and Rehana are friends.
    Last term they both did ten homeworks for geography.

    Aleyha's marks had a mean of 6.8 and a range of 1.
    Rehana's marks were:

       9, 1, 0, 8, 8, 9, 8, 7, 2, 8

   (a) Work out:
       (i)   the range of Rehana's marks
       (ii)   the mean of Rehana's marks
       (iii) the mode of Rehana's marks
       (iv)   the median of Rehana's marks.
   (b) Comment on which friend might have done best.

Summary of key points

1 The mode of a set of data is the value which occurs most often.

2 In a bar chart the mode is the value with the highest bar.

3 In a frequency table, the mode is the value with the highest frequency.

4 The median is the middle value when the data is arranged in order of size.

5 $\text{Mean} = \dfrac{\text{sum of values}}{\text{number of values}}$

6 Range = highest value − lowest value

16 Using and applying mathematics

In this Unit you will learn about the process behind doing a mathematical investigation.

This is the problem that you will be investigating:

Shaking hands

Andrea has a birthday party:

She asks each of her friends to shake hands with everyone else just once.

Investigate to find the relationship between the number of friends and the number of handshakes.

The first step is to:

Understand the problem

The best way to understand the problem is to just have a go.
Suppose Andrea has invited four friends:
Bronwen, Charlie, Dipesh and Elaine.

Five of the possible handshakes could be:

    Andrea and Bronwen
    Andrea and Charlie
    Andrea and Dipesh
    Andrea and Elaine
    Bronwen and Charlie

Exercise 16A

1   Find the other five handshakes to show that there are ten possible handshakes when there are four friends.

Make the problem as simple as you can

To help you understand the problem, try out the simplest cases first.

Example 1

How many handshakes will there be if Andrea invites one friend, Bronwen?

There will be one handshake:

    Andrea and Bronwen

Example 2

How many handshakes will there be if Andrea invites Charlie as well, so there are two friends?

The handshakes will be:

    Andrea and Bronwen
    Andrea and Charlie
    Bronwen and Charlie

So there will be three handshakes if Andrea invites two friends

Exercise 16B

1   List all the handshakes if Andrea invites three friends: Bronwen, Charlie and Dipesh.

    How many handshakes are there with three friends?

Plan and use a strategy

A strategy is an ordered approach to a problem.

Imagine trying to work out how many handshakes there would be at this party!

Using a strategy will mean that you don't miss any handshakes.

Example 3

How many handshakes will there be if Andrea invites five friends: Bronwen, Charlie, Dipesh, Elaine and Flora?

The strategy will be:

Count all of Andrea's handshakes first.
Then count all of Bronwen's.
Then count all of Charlie's.
And so on ...
To save time just use the first letter of each name:
AF = Andrea and Flora
The handshakes for each person are:

Andrea:	AB	AC	AD	AE	AF	5
Bronwen:	BC	BD	BE	BF		4
Charlie:	CD	CE	CF			3
Dipesh:	DE	DF				2
Elaine:	EF					1

Hint:
You don't need to do BA as Bronwen has already shaken hands with Andrea.

Flora has already shaken hands with everyone.

So the number of handshakes for 5 friends is:

$$5 + 4 + 3 + 2 + 1 = 15$$

Exercise 16C

1 (a) Use this strategy to check the results so far:

Number of friends:	1	2	3	4	5
Number of handshakes:	1	3	6	10	15

(b) Use the strategy to show that there will be 21 handshakes if Andrea invites a sixth friend, Graham.

Record your results

Once you have started to get some results it is best to record them in a table.

Exercise 16D

1   Copy and complete this table:

Number of friends	Number of handshakes
1	1
2	3
3	6
6	

Always make sure your tables are clearly labelled.

Make predictions

Once you have your results in a table you should see if you can find any patterns.

A simple pattern to see here is that the number of handshakes grows as the number of friends grows.

The number of handshakes also follows a pattern:

1	3	6	10	15	21
odd	odd	even	even	odd	odd

which is not so obvious.

You can use your observations to make **predictions**.

Example 4

Predict whether the number of handshakes will be odd or even for seven friends.

The results so far are:

Number of friends	Number of handshakes	Odd or even
1	1	odd
2	3	odd
3	6	even
4	10	even
5	15	odd
6	21	odd
7		even

Even though you don't know the number of handshakes you can predict that it will be an even number.

Exercise 16E

1 Predict whether there will be an odd or even number when there are:

   (a) 10 friends   **(b)** 20 friends   **(c)** 50 friends

   Show how you get your answers.

   A good way to find patterns in number sequences is to use **differences**. You can see a pattern in your results if you find the difference between each pair of numbers.

Number of friends	1	2	3	4	5	6
Number of handshakes	1	3	6	10	15	21

   +2   +3   +4   +5   +6

   The number of handshakes increases by a simple pattern   2, 3, 4, 5, 6, ...

   You can use this to predict that for 7 friends there will be $21 + 7 = 28$ handshakes.

Example 5

How many handshakes will there be for 8 friends?

Use the pattern to make a prediction:

$$\begin{array}{ccccccccc} & +2 & +3 & +4 & +5 & +6 & +7 & +8 & \\ 1 & 3 & 6 & 10 & 15 & 21 & 28 & 36 \text{ handshakes} \end{array}$$

If you know the pattern and the first answer you can find the answer without drawing out the whole table each time.

Exercise 16F

1 Use a pattern to predict how many handshakes there will be for:

   (a) 8 friends   (b) 9 friends   (c) 10 friends

Testing predictions

Whenever you make a prediction you should test it to check whether it is a good one.

Example 6

Test the prediction that there will be 28 handshakes if Andrea invites 7 friends.

Use the strategy to count the handshakes.

Andrea:	AB	AC	AD	AE	AF	AG	AH
Bronwen:	BC	BD	BE	BF	BG	BH	
Charlie:	CD	CE	CF	CG	CH		
Dipesh:	DE	DF	DG	DH			
Elaine:	EF	EG	EH				
Flora:	FG	FH					
Graham:	GH						

Herbert has already shaken hands with everyone.

There are 28 pairs of letters so there are 28 handshakes when Andrea invites 7 friends.
The prediction was a good one!

Exercise 16G

▶1 Using the strategy, test the predictions that you made for:

(a) 8 friends   **(b)** 9 friends   **(c)** 10 friends

Making a generalization

Once you have tested a prediction you can make a **generalization**. You can make some generalizations about shaking hands:

- The bigger the number of friends the bigger the number of handshakes.
- The number of handshakes follows the pattern odd, odd, even, even.
- You can find the number of handshakes by finding

  $1 + 2 + 3 + 4 + 5 + \ldots$

  stopping at the number of friends invited to the party.

The last generalization means that you can work out the number of handshakes just by knowing the number of friends invited.

You may also have noticed that there is a pattern to the answers. Look at the answers up to four friends:

One friend:
Andrea: AB
Bronwen:

Two friends:
Andrea: AB   AC
Bronwen: BC
Charlie:

Three friends:
Andrea: AB   AC   AD
Bronwen: BC   BD
Charlie: CD
Dipesh:

Remember:
The last friend has already shaken hands with everyone.

Four friends:

Andrea:	AB	AC	AD	AE
Bronwen:	BC	BD	BE	
Charlie:	CD	CE		
Dipesh:	DE			
Elaine:				

The number of handshakes forms a triangular pattern.
The numbers 1, 3, 6, 10, 15 ... are called the **triangular numbers**.

Triangular number	1st	2nd	3rd	4th	5th
Value	1	3	6	10	15
Pattern	•	• • •	• • • • • •	• • • • • • • • • •	• • • • • • • • • • • • • • •

So any generalization about the number of handshakes is a generalization about triangular numbers and vice versa.

Look at the pattern for the
4th triangular number, 10:

You can repeat the triangle upside
down to make a rectangle:

The number of dots in the rectangle is:

$$4 \times 5 = 20$$

The rectangle is made from two triangles so divide by two:

$$\tfrac{1}{2} \times 20 = 10$$

which is the 4th triangular number.

Example 7

Show that the 3rd triangular number is $\dfrac{3 \times 4}{2}$.

The dot pattern is:

● ● ●
● ●
●

Make the rectangle:

● ● ●
● ● ●
● ● ●
● ● ●

The rectangle has $3 \times 4 = 12$ dots, so

the 3rd triangular number $= \dfrac{3 \times 4}{2} = 6$.

Exercise 16H

1   Show that:

(a) the fifth triangular number $= \dfrac{5 \times 6}{2}$

(b) the sixth triangular number $= \dfrac{6 \times 7}{2}$

Try to make a generalization from your results:

1st triangular number $= \dfrac{1 \times 2}{2}$

2nd triangular number $= \dfrac{2 \times 3}{2}$

3rd triangular number $= \dfrac{3 \times 4}{2}$

4th triangular number $= \dfrac{4 \times 5}{2}$

As the number of handshakes follows the pattern for the triangular numbers you can predict a rule:

Number of handshakes $= \dfrac{\text{number of friends} \times (\text{number of friends} + 1)}{2}$

Exercise 16I

1   Use this rule to check your earlier answers for
    (a) 5 friends   **(b)** 6 friends   **(c)** 7 friends
    (d) 8 friends   **(e)** 9 friends   **(f)** 10 friends

    The predicted rule works so you have a generalization
    that lets you work out the number of handshakes
    without having to add $1 + 2 + 3 + 4 + 5 + \ldots$

Summary

The steps you should take in any mathematical
investigation are:

- Understand the problem – have a go.
- Make the problem as simple as you can.
- Use an ordered approach – plan a strategy.
- Record your results – make a table.
- Make predictions.
- Test your predictions.
- Try and make a generalization.

17 Calculators and computers

This unit shows you some ways of using scientific calculators, graphical calculators and computer software to help build on and extend the work you have been studying in the other units of this book.

The examples will work on Casio calculators, the spreadsheet examples are based on Microsoft Excel and the examples for drawing angles, polygons and triangles work with WinLogo.

17.1 Using your square root key

You can find square roots using the  key.

On some older calculators you have to enter the number before pressing the 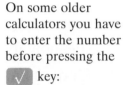 key:

Answer: 5

Some calculators have only one key for square roots and squares. Check whether you need to press the SHIFT key before the

 key.

Get to know your calculator!

Example 1

Find:

(a) $\sqrt{25}$ **(b)** $\sqrt{4} + \sqrt{9}$ **(c)** $\sqrt{(3^2 + 4^2)}$

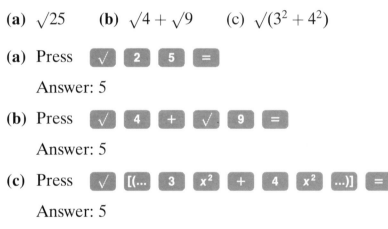

(a) Press

Answer: 5

(b) Press

Answer: 5

(c) Press

Answer: 5

Exercise 17A

1   Calculate:

(a) $\sqrt{324}$ (b) $\sqrt{1369}$

(c) $\sqrt{576}$ (d) $\sqrt{2304} - \sqrt{289}$

(e) $\sqrt{(6^2 + 8^2)}$ (f) $\sqrt{(5^2 + 12^2)}$

(g) $\sqrt{25} + \sqrt{144}$ (h) $\sqrt{441} \div \sqrt{49}$

2   Investigate what happens if you keep taking the square root starting with any 10-digit number?

Press the 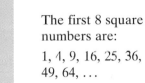 key, enter your 10-digit number, press

= , √ , Ans , √ , Ans , ...

3   Use square numbers for *a* and *b* to investigate if
(a) $\sqrt{(a \times b)} = \sqrt{a} \times \sqrt{b}$
(b) $\sqrt{(a + b)} = \sqrt{a} + \sqrt{b}$
(c) $\sqrt{(a \div b)} = \sqrt{a} \div \sqrt{b}$
(d) $\sqrt{(a - b)} = \sqrt{a} - \sqrt{b}$

The first 8 square numbers are:
1, 4, 9, 16, 25, 36, 49, 64, ...

17.2   Using your powers key

You can calculate the value of numbers like 3^5 using the  key.

Remember:
3^5 means
$3 \times 3 \times 3 \times 3 \times 3$

Example 2

Find:
(a) 3^5 (b) $4^3 + 9^4$ (c) $8^6 \div 2^4$

(a) Press:

3 x^y 5 =

Answer: 243

(b) Press:

4 x^y 3 + 9 x^y 4 =

Answer: 6625

(c) Press:

Answer: 16 384

Exercise 17B   Scientific calculator

1 (a) Calculate 6^3 (b) Calculate 8^7
   (c) Calculate $10^3 + 10^5$ (d) Calculate $6^8 \div 3^5$

2 (a) Which is bigger 2^{30} or 3^{20} ?
   (b) By how much?

3 (a) Calculate $(2^3)^4$ (b) Calculate $(2^4)^3$ (c) Calculate $(4^3)^2$

4 If n is a positive whole number what is the **smallest**
   value of n which makes 4^n bigger than 5^{12} ?

5 (a) Calculate 100^1
   (b) Calculate $1^{1^{1^{...}}}$
   (c) Calculate a^0, where a is any positive whole number.

6 (a) In the book *One Grain of Rice: A Mathematical
       Folktale* by Demi (Illustrator), a young woman
       called Rani outwitted the Raja to gain food
       for her starving people. Rani demanded that
       she be given 1 grain of rice on day 1 and each
       day after for a total of thirty days the number
       of grains of rice given should be doubled.
       Calculate the total number of grains of rice
       Rani obtained for her people.

   The total rice is
   $1 + 2 + 4 + 8 + 16 + \ldots$
   or, in power notation,
   $2^0 + 2^1 + 2^2 + 2^3 + 2^4 + $
   $+ \ldots + 2^{29}$

   (b) A packet of rice contains approximately
       17 000 grains. Approximately how many packets
       would be required to obtain the equivalent amount
       of rice in modern times?

7 What do you notice about the digits in the questions
   and answers if you calculate:
   (a) $3^3 + 4^4 + 3^3 + 5^5$
   (b) $88^2 + 33^2$
   (c) $4^4 + 3^3 + 8^8 + 5^5 + 7^7 + 9^9 + 0^0 + 8^8 + 8^8$
   (d) 567^2
   (e) 854^2 ?

   Entering 0^0 on your
   calculator may give
   an error.
   Enter 0 instead.

8 For $n = 1$ to 10, which of $2^n - 1$ are prime
   numbers?

   There is more about
   prime numbers on
   page 53.

Exercise 17C   Scientific calculator

1 **This exercise has something to do with square roots!**

- Continue this sequence for a further 10 terms

$$\frac{1}{1}, \frac{3}{2}, \frac{7}{5}, \frac{17}{12}, \ldots\ldots$$

- Calculate the decimal equivalent of each term, correct to 8 decimal places.

- Terms 9 and 10 have the same value, correct to 5 decimal places. What is this value an approximation to? This value is called the **limit** of the sequence, correct to 5 decimal places. Extending your sequence will give a more accurate limit.

- Choose a different fraction from any in your list to start the sequence again. Does this produce a different limit to the original sequence?

- Starting with $\frac{1}{1}$, what is the limit of the sequence if this time you **treble** the denominator before adding the numerator? The rule to obtain the new denominator remains the same as before.

- Extend the above idea to investigate what happens if you consider other multiples of the numerator.

How to get from one fraction to the next:

From $\frac{7}{5}$,

- Double the denominator and add the numerator to obtain the new numerator:
  $2 \times 5 + 7 = 17$
- Add the numerator to the denominator to obtain the new denominator:
  $7 + 5 = 12$

The next fraction is therefore $\frac{17}{12}$

The decimal equivalent of a fraction is the result when the numerator of the fraction is divided by the denominator of the fraction.

The decimal equivalent of $\frac{7}{5}$ is 1.2.

2 **(a)** For the Fibonacci sequence 1, 1, 2, 3, 5, 8, 13, 21, ..., choose any 10 consecutive terms. What is the connection between the sum of these 10 numbers and the seventh number in your sequence?

You will need to try at least 3 sets of different numbers from the sequence.

(b) Create your own Fibonacci type sequence using any two starting numbers. Is the connection between the sum and the seventh term still true?

Example:

5, 7, 12, 19, 31, 50, ...

17.3 Generating sequences

You can use a spreadsheet to generate sequences.

Exercise 17D   Spreadsheet

1   For the sequences displayed in columns A to G below enter:
    * the first term of each sequence into the first row of a spreadsheet
    * a formula to generate each sequence into the second row
    * use your formulae to generate the first 30 terms of each sequence.

There is more on sequences on page 83.

	A	B	C	D	E	F	G
1	12	40	4	−6	−6	1	1
2	13	38	8	−3	−9	3	2
3	14	36	16	0	−12	7	5
4	15	34	32	3	−15	15	14

Enter these numbers in row 1

Enter the formulae in row 2
Example: = a1 + 1 in cell A2

A quick way to copy formulae is to drag this black square down; to cell A30 in this case

2   Generate the first 100 terms of these sequences. Begin by entering the number 1 in cells A2, B2, C2 and C3.

There is more on the triangular numbers on page 261.

	A	B	C
1	Positive whole numbers	Triangular numbers	Fibonacci sequence
2	1	1	1
3	2	3	1
4	3	6	2
5	4	10	3
6	5	15	5
7	6	21	8
8	7	28	13
9	8	36	21
10	9	45	34

* Use a formula in cell A3 to generate the positive whole numbers.
* Use a formula in B3, linked to column A, to help generate the triangular numbers.
* Use a formula in cell C4 to generate the Fibonacci sequence.

3   In cell D2 enter a formula to square each term of the Fibonacci sequence. Copy the formula down to cell D10. Find another connection between the terms in column D and the terms in the Fibonacci sequence.

4   Why is it not possible to use a spreadsheet to generate the first 100 prime numbers?

17.4   Percentage increase and decrease

Example 3

Page 131 shows you how to increase and decrease by a percentage.

Here is another method:

- To **increase** by 8% multiply by 1.08 [1 + 0.08]
- To **decrease** by 8% multiply by 0.92 [1 − 0.08]
- To **increase** by 12% multiply by 1.12 [1 + 0.12]
- To **decrease** by 12% multiply by 0.88 [1 − 0.12]

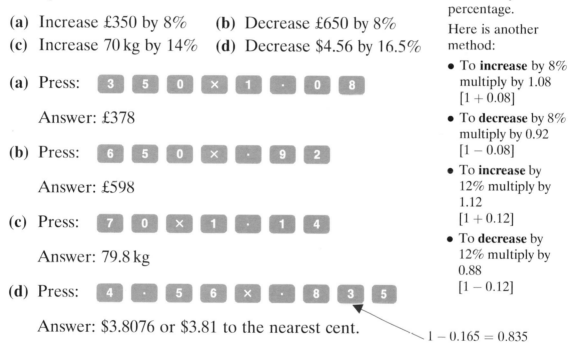

(a) Increase £350 by 8%   (b) Decrease £650 by 8%
(c) Increase 70 kg by 14%   (d) Decrease $4.56 by 16.5%

(a) Press: `3` `5` `0` `×` `1` `.` `0` `8`

Answer: £378

(b) Press: `6` `5` `0` `×` `.` `9` `2`

Answer: £598

(c) Press: `7` `0` `×` `1` `.` `1` `4`

Answer: 79.8 kg

(d) Press: `4` `.` `5` `6` `×` `.` `8` `3` `5`

Answer: $3.8076 or $3.81 to the nearest cent. $1 − 0.165 = 0.835$

Exercise 17E   Scientific calculator

1   Computer prices are reduced in a sale by 12%. Before the sale a computer was priced at £2650. What is its sale price?

2   Last year Matthew weighed 65.4 kg and his height was 1.65 m. This year his weight has increased by 2% and his height by 3.5%. Calculate his present weight to the nearest gram and his present height to the nearest centimetre.

3   Ali was earning £26 500 a year when he was given a pay increase of 3%.
    What is his new salary?

4 In the 1998/1999 soccer season the average home attendance for a team was 32 456. The following season this increased by 7%.
What was the new average attendance?

5 Anna-Natasha put £3658 in a Building Society. Each year her money increased by 6%. How much money, to the nearest penny, does Anna-Natasha have in her account after: **(a)** 1 year **(b)** 2 years **(c)** 5 years

6 Joshua went into his local interactive games store and bought 2 light guns at £14.99 each, 5 CD-R games at £17.99 each, 1 dual shock analogue joy pad for £18.99, 6 memory cards at £10.95 each and 2 scart cables for £7.98 each. He was given a discount of 9% on the total. What was his final bill to the nearest penny?

Remember to press the equals sign before calculating the discount.

17.5 Number machines

You can use a spreadsheet to find the output of a number machine.

There is more on number machines on page 78.

Example 4

input   output

2 ➤ × 0.8 ➤ 1.6

4 ➤ 3.2

6 ➤ 4.8

8 ➤ 6.4

10 ➤ 8

To produce the inputs and outputs above:

Enter 2 in cell A1 and the two formulae in cells A2 and B1.

	A	B
1	2	=A1*0.8
2	=A1+2	

Copy down the formula in cell A2 to A5 and the formula in B1 to B5.

	A	B
1	2	=A1*0.8
2	=A1+2	=A2*0.8
3	=A2+2	=A3*0.8
4	=A3+2	=A4*0.8
5	=A4+2	=A5*0.8

This will produce the required inputs and outputs in column A and column B.

	A	B
1	2	1.6
2	4	3.2
3	6	4.8
4	8	6.4
5	10	8

Exercise 17F   Spreadsheet

Use a spreadsheet to find the output for these number machines:

1 **(a)**

input	rule	output
3	× by 0.6	
6		
9		
12		
15		

(b)

input	rule	output
12	÷ by 0.8	
10		
8		
6		
4		

(c)

input	rule	output
5	increase	
10	by 5%	
15		
20		
25		

(d)

input	rule	output
10 000	decrease	
2000	by 12%	
400		
80		
16		

Remember to work out the rule for the input column so that you can enter that formula in your spreadsheet. The formula for the output column comes from the given rule.

2 Use the inputs in Question **1(a)** and the rule 'multiply by 3 and then subtract 4'.

3 Use the inputs in Question **1(a)** and the rule 'subtract 4 and then multiply by 3'.

4 Use the inputs in Question **1(b)** and the rule 'multiply by 1.6 and then divide by 1.6'.

5 Use the inputs in Question **1(c)** and the rule 'increase by 10% and then decrease by 10%'.

In questions 2 to 5 use three columns:
- Input
- First output
- Second output

17.6   Handling data

You can use a spreadsheet to calculate the mean, median, mode and range for given data.

Exercise 17G   Spreadsheet

1 **(a)** Enter the following data in cells A1 to A10 on a spreadsheet

3, 5, 7, 12, 17, 17, 22, 26, 27, 85

(b) In cell A11 enter a formula to calculate the mean of the data.

(c) In cell A12 enter a formula to calculate the median of the data.

(d) In cell A13 enter a formula to calculate the mode of the data.

In Microsoft Excel the formulae are:
- =average(A1:A10) to calculate the mean
- =median(A1:A10) to calculate the median
- =mode(A1:A10) to calculate the mode
- =A10−A1 to give the range

(e) In cell A14 enter a formula to calculate the range of the data.

(f) Which is the fairest type of average? Why?

There is more about averages on page 238.

2   Repeat steps (a) to (f) above in columns B to D. Make:

   (i)   column B the original data multiplied by 10 ◄

   (ii) column C the original data plus 3

   (iii) column D 5 times the original data plus 2.

   (iv) Comment on your answers.

Here the data is ten times bigger than the original data. Will the averages be 10 times bigger?

3   Use the data on extreme weather conditions given in the table below to create a scatter graph on a spreadsheet of:

   (a) the number of millimetres of rain against the number of minutes of rainfall.

   (b) the number of millimetres of rain against the date of the month.

   (c) Comment on the type of correlation for each graph, giving reasons.

The different types of correlation can be found in Section 12.6

Intense rainfall in minutes (UK)

Minutes	mm	LOCATION	Date	Month	Year
5	32	Preston (Lancashire)	10	AUG	1893
12	51	Wisbech (Cambridgeshire)	27	JUN	1970
15	56	Bolton (Greater Manchester)	18	JUL	1964
20	63	Sidcup (Kent)	5	SEP	1958
20	63	Hindolveston (Norfolk)	11	JUL	1959
25	67	Pershore (Worcestershire)	11	JUN	1970
30	80	Eskdalemuir (Dumfries)	26	JUN	1953
45	97	Orra Beg (Antrim)	1	AUG	1980
60	92	Maidenhead (Berkshire)	12	JUL	1901
75	102	Wisley (Surrey)	16	JUL	1947
75	95	Ilkley (North Yorkshire)	12	JUL	1900

If you are working at a computer that is on-line you can paste the data directly into your spreadsheet from http://www.rhegeds. freeserve.co.uk/ extremes.htm

90	117	Dunsop Valley (Lancashire)	8	AUG	1967
90	111	Miserden (Gloucestershire)	10	JUN	1970
100	116	West Wickham (London)	22	JUL	1934
105	116	Sevenoaks (Kent)	25	JUN	1980
120	131	Knockholt (Kent)	5	SEP	1958
120	155	Hewenden Reservoir (Yorkshire)	11	JUNE	1956
120	193	Walshaw Dean Lodge (Yorkshire)	19	MAY	1989
155	169	Hampstead (London)	14	AUG	1975
180	178	Horncastle (Lincolnshire)	7	OCT	1960

In part **(b)** use the Ctrl key to highlight the two columns which are not next to each other.

17.7 Angles and polygons

You can draw angles, triangles and polygons on a computer using the program WinLogo.

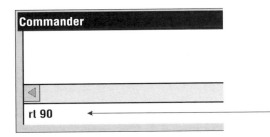

Type your instructions here and then press the Enter key before typing your next instruction.

In WinLogo you must provide instructions to move the 'turtle' around the screen.

The turtle begins this way round:

rt 90
will turn it 90° clockwise:

fd 100
will move it forward '100' places and draw a line '100' units long:

Example 5

Draw on screen:

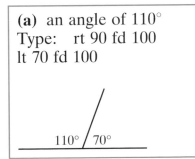

(a) an angle of 110°
Type: rt 90 fd 100
lt 70 fd 100

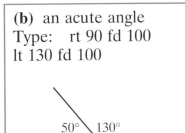

(b) an acute angle
Type: rt 90 fd 100
lt 130 fd 100

Exercise 17H   WinLogo

1 Use WinLogo to draw:

(a) an angle of 165°   **(b)** an angle of 50°

(c) an angle of 215°   **(d)** a right-angle

(e) an equilateral triangle of side 110 units

(f) a square of side 150 units

(g) a regular hexagon of side 140 units

(h) a regular octagon of side 100 units

(i) a tessellation pattern

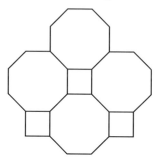

A tessellation pattern is when polygons fit together with no gaps between them.

It is a good idea to plan these on paper first, as you need to work out the angle to turn through!

cs will clear the screen.

A quick way to draw the square in part (e) is to type repeat 4[fd 150 rt 90]

The gaps are important in the coding above.

The other polygons can be done in a similar way.

17.8   Straight lines

You can draw lines on a graphical calculator. After you have switched on the calculator select the **GRAPH** icon using the arrow keys and then press the **EXE** key to display a window similar to this:

```
G-Func  :Y=
Y1:
Y2:
Y3:
Y4:
SEL DEL          DRAW
```

Press SHIFT **F3** to bring up the V-Window:

```
V-Window
Xmin:          −5
max:            5
scl:            1
INIT TRIG Sto Rcl
```

Press **EXE** to bring up the G-Func menu again.

Change the size of the *x*-axis to a minimum of −5 and a maximum of 5, using the **EXE** key to confirm each entry.

Use a scale of 1

Press the down arrow key to produce a similar window for *y* and change the *y*-axis from −5 to 5, using a scale of 1, again.

Exercise 17I   Graphical calculator

1   Draw four different lines parallel to $y = x + 1$

2   Draw four different lines parallel to $y = 2x - 1$

3   Draw four different lines non-parallel lines but all passing through the point (0, 2)

4   Draw four different lines with a steeper gradient than $y = x$ and all passing through the origin.

5   Draw four different lines with a shallower gradient than $y = x$.

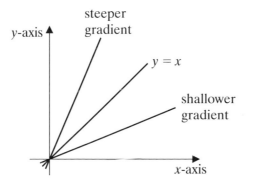

To begin question **1**, press

to store the equation Y1 = X + 3.
Now type similar equations for Y2, Y3 and Y4.

Finally press **F4** to to produce your four lines.

Press

to return to the GRAPH Mode and delete your equations onc by one by using the arrow keys to select the equations and then the **F2** key followed by the **F1** key.

An alternative way to do this exercise is to use a computer software package like Omnigraph.

You can also use a spreadsheet to draw graphs. You will have to create the points in a similar way to Unit 11 by using the columns on your spreadsheet. Example 3 on page 176 could be produced as follows:

	A	B
1	x	y
2	−3	−3
3	−2	−1
4	−1	1
5	0	3
6	1	5
7	2	7
8	3	9

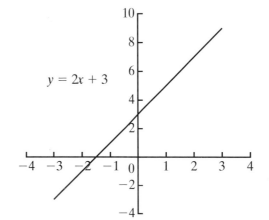

- −3 was entered in cell A2.
- = A2 + 1 was entered in cell A3.
- = 2*A2 + 3 was entered in cell B2.

17.9 Fractions

Example 6

(a) Find $\frac{2}{3}$ of £39.81

(b) Reduce $\frac{90}{135}$ to its lowest terms.

(c) Place the following fractions in order of size, starting with the smallest:

$\frac{11}{13}, \frac{7}{9}, \frac{21}{26}, \frac{6}{7}, \frac{16}{19}$

(d) Change the mixed number $16\frac{12}{17}$ into an improper fraction.

(e) Change $\frac{423}{17}$ to a mixed number.

(f) Calculate $\frac{5}{11} + \frac{11}{13}$

You can use the fraction key on your calculator to answer the type of questions you met in Unit 6.

Your fraction key may look like this

$\boxed{\text{a}^{b/c}}$

The fraction button will reduce a fraction to its lowest terms. For a set of equivalent fractions, the one where the numerator and denominator can not be reduced any more is the fraction in its lowest terms:

$\frac{15}{20} = \frac{12}{16} = \frac{9}{12} = \frac{6}{8} = \frac{3}{4}$ ◂┘

(a) Press

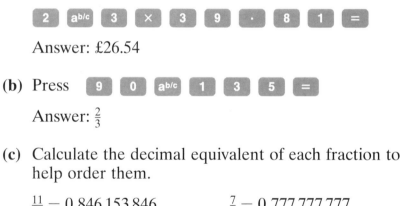

Answer: £26.54

Press the multiplication key for 'of' in $\frac{2}{3}$ of £39.81

(b) Press $\boxed{9}\ \boxed{0}\ \boxed{\text{a}^{b/c}}\ \boxed{1}\ \boxed{3}\ \boxed{5}\ \boxed{=}$

Answer: $\frac{2}{3}$

(c) Calculate the decimal equivalent of each fraction to help order them.

$\frac{11}{13} = 0.846\,153\,846\ldots$ $\frac{7}{9} = 0.777\,777\,777\ldots$

$\frac{21}{26} = 0.807\,692\,307\ldots$ $\frac{6}{7} = 0.857\,142\,857\ldots$

$\frac{16}{19} = 0.842\,105\,263\ldots$

Answer: $\frac{7}{9}, \frac{21}{26}, \frac{16}{19}, \frac{11}{13}, \frac{6}{7}$

Divide the numerator by the denominator to find a fraction's decimal equivalent.

(d) Press $\boxed{1}\ \boxed{6}\ \boxed{\times}\ \boxed{1}\ \boxed{7}\ \boxed{+}\ \boxed{1}\ \boxed{2}\ \boxed{=}$

Answer $= \frac{284}{17}$

(e) Press ⬜4 ⬜2 ⬜3 ⬜aᵇ/c ⬜1 ⬜7 ⬜=

Answer = $24\frac{15}{17}$

(f) Press ⬜5 ⬜aᵇ/c ⬜1 ⬜1 ⬜+ ⬜1 ⬜1 ⬜aᵇ/c ⬜1 ⬜3 ⬜=

Answer: $1\frac{43}{143}$

Exercise 17J   Scientific calculator

1   Calculate:

    (a) $\frac{3}{5}$ of £63.45

    (b) $\frac{7}{9}$ of £167.76

    (c) $\frac{11}{12}$ of $625.32

2   Reduce these fractions to their lowest terms:

    (a) $\frac{140}{252}$ **(b)** $\frac{176}{192}$

    (c) $\frac{264}{282}$ **(d)** $\frac{57}{76}$

    (e) $\frac{315}{560}$

3   Place these fractions in order of size starting with the smallest:

    $\frac{27}{28}$ $\frac{35}{36}$ $\frac{16}{17}$ $\frac{12}{13}$ $\frac{55}{59}$

4   Change these mixed numbers to improper fractions:

    (a) $13\frac{5}{9}$ **(b)** $23\frac{14}{17}$

    (c) $9\frac{17}{19}$ **(d)** $45\frac{56}{57}$

5   Change these improper fractions to mixed numbers:

    (a) $\frac{165}{132}$ **(b)** $\frac{203}{19}$

    (c) $\frac{433}{212}$ **(d)** $\frac{1965}{18}$

6   Calculate:

    (a) $\frac{3}{11} + \frac{15}{16}$ **(b)** $\frac{21}{43} - \frac{17}{45}$

    (c) $\frac{7}{12} + \frac{13}{17} + \frac{9}{10}$ **(d)** $\frac{12}{13} - \frac{1}{17} + \frac{5}{9}$

Exercise 17K   Scientific calculator

The 24 Puzzle

1	2	3	4
5	6	7	8
9	1	2	3
4	5	6	7
8	9	1	2
3	4	5	6
7	8	9	1
2	3	4	5
6	7	8	9

Shaded are some possible grouping of 4 numbers.

In the table above

- Select any block of four numbers.

- Using **all** four numbers and any of the mathematical signs $+$, $-$, $\times$, $\div$ create a total of 24.

Example 1:

1	2	3	4

$$1 \times 2 \times 3 \times 4 = 24$$

Example 2:

7	8
2	3

$$(7 - 3) \times (8 - 2) = 24$$

- You may use brackets.

- Placing two digits together to make a number like 36 is not allowed.

Index